HOw TO
GET BETTER VALUE
HEALTHCARE

Second Edition

J.A. MUIR GRAY
Kt, CBE, DSc, MD

This edition takes into account the principles and proposals in *Equity and Excellence: Liberating the NHS*, presented to Parliament by the Secretary of State for Health by Command of Her Majesty, July 2010, Command 7881

OFFOX PRESS

First published 2007
Second Edition 2011

Published by Offox Press for Better Value Healthcare Ltd.

Email: books@offoxpress.com
www.offoxpress.com

A CIP catalogue record for this book is available from the British Library.

ISBN-13: 9781904202066

Printed and bound in Great Britain by Information Press, Eynsham, Oxford.

Other titles and training programmes in preparation include:

How To Build Healthcare Systems

How To Create The Right Healthcare Culture

How To Practise Population Medicine

How To Manage Knowledge in a Health Service

Preface

Language evolves; new terms appear and mutate. Some flourish and spread, terms like effectiveness spread like a virus following the publication of Archie Cochrane's classic, *Effectiveness and Efficiency*. Others, many of them management terms, mercifully become extinct. For the last twenty years the terms cost effectiveness, quality and safety have flourished, and rightly so, but there is now a new term that will become the pre-eminent term for the next twenty years and that term is 'value'. The concept will not make extinct the dominant words of the last fifty years, it will embrace and include them as Michael Porter eloquently describes:

> *Value in any field must be defined around the customer, not the supplier. Value must also be measured by outputs, not inputs. Hence it is patient health results that matter, not the volume of services delivered. But results are achieved at some cost. Therefore, the proper objective is the value of health care delivery, or the patient health outcomes relative to the total cost (inputs) of attaining those outcomes. Efficiency, then, is subsumed in the concept of value. So are other objectives like safety, which is one aspect of outcomes.*(1)

The remorseless process of natural selection was summarised in October 2010 by Robert Brook of the RAND Corporation, who was one of the pioneers of the quality revolution twenty years ago, in a leading article in the prestigious *Journal of the American Medical Association* entitled 'The end of the quality improvement movement – long live improving value'. (2)

Since the first edition of this book was published there has been one significant event which has put value on everyone's agenda – the global economic meltdown. In every country 'value' is the key concept and increasing value by improving outcome and reducing expenditure are the key challenges for those who pay for or manage care, including citizens and patients.

(1)   Porter, M.E. (2008) *What is Value in Health Care?* Harvard Business School. Institute for Strategy and Competitiveness. White Paper.

(2)   Brook, R.H. (2010) The end of the quality improvement movement. *JAMA* 304:1831-1832

J.A. Muir Gray

Contents

1

THE 21st CENTURY HEALTHCARE CRISIS

This chapter will:

- set out the challenges faced by health services, now and in the next decade;
- describe the causes of increasing need and demand;
- explain what is meant by the 'third healthcare revolution'.

By the end of this chapter you will have an understanding of:

- the pressures on health services and their resources;
- the drivers of need and demand which can be mitigated;
- the importance of climate change to people who invest in or manage health services;
- how to explain to people about the third healthcare revolution and how they can be harnessed to help narrow the gap between need and demand on the one hand, and limited resources on the other.

20th century healthcare was dominated by clinicians, effectiveness, and efficiency. 21st century healthcare will be dominated by patients, outcomes and value, because the challenges facing 21st century healthcare in every society are massive and growing. Since the first edition of this book in 2007, two dramatic global events occurred which will change the nature of healthcare more than any single scientific discovery. These were the economic crunch, and the explicit acceptance by the United States and China that climate change poses the biggest single threat to health and wellbeing. The consequences of these dramatic events will shape how we respond to the inexorable increase in need and demand.

In the United Kingdom, the global economic problems have had a big impact which has led to a change in government and a budget, shortly after the election in June 2010, which signalled a reduction in public spending, with the NHS being treated as one of a small number of budgets which would not be cut. In the White Paper on *Equity and Excellence: Liberating the NHS*, published in the next month, there was an explicit commitment that *'we will increase health spending in real terms in each year of this Parliament'*.

Furthermore, even if much more money could be made available, the human resources might not be forthcoming. As societies become richer, fewer people are willing to carry out the basic tasks, often aesthetically unsavoury, involved in caring for sick people. As a result, many developed countries have taken to plundering the human resources of poorer countries, employing a significant proportion of the medical and nursing graduates from poor countries. Fortunately, some countries now regard this as something which is undesirable, whereas formerly it was accepted as an economic necessity. Even if recruitment were to continue, however, the basic premise remains the same and is demonstrated in Figure 1.1. Need and demand are increasing faster than the resources available to meet them.

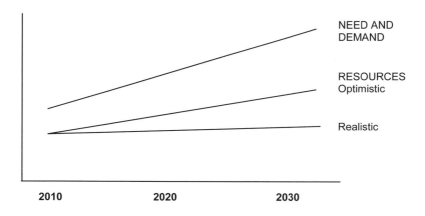

Figure 1.1 The widening gap between resources and need

Increasing need

From population ageing

In almost every society, the number of people aged over 80 is increasing dramatically. The main reason for this trend is not that the death rate of people in their seventies is declining as a result of better medical care; it is because the percentage of children who survived the perilous years of infancy rose significantly seven decades ago.

There is good evidence that people aged over eighty are fitter now than people aged over eighty were twenty or thirty years ago. However, even fitter old people have a higher prevalence of chronic disease, so the number of people suffering from chronic diseases increases as a result of population ageing. In addition, whether people die at 70, 80, or 90 years of age, the last few months of life is a time in which there is usually heavy, but not always appropriate, use of health services. An increase in the number of people surviving to old age inevitably increases need.

From new diseases

21st century healthcare has to cope not only with the diseases it inherited from the 20th century but also with new diseases. Indeed, in many poor countries, health services still have to cope not only with the 19th century epidemics of tuberculosis, cholera, and infant malnutrition, but also with heart disease and road traffic accidents. In developed countries, health services have to cope with the problems that have evolved in the 20th century as a consequence of lifestyle changes and population ageing. However, the list is not closed.

The last decades have seen the emergence of AIDS, drug resistant TB and Avian flu, and the evolution of problems in which social changes, the media, and the evangelical work of some clinicians have led to epidemics of new conditions, such as anorexia nervosa and false memory syndrome. The evolution of these epidemics, each a real problem for the affected individual, is acutely analysed in *Hystories* by Elaine Showalter. (1)

From new technology

A useful definition of a health need is a health problem for which there is an effective intervention. For this reason, when a new drug or other type of medical technology is invented and approved for use, a new need is also created.

Managing need

There is very little that those who pay for or manage healthcare can do to slow the increase in need. If those who pay for healthcare are also responsible for the public health, they need to do what they can to prevent the epidemics of smoking-related diseases, or diseases related to addiction, or the consequences of obesity, for each of these will have a massive impact on healthcare. If the payers for healthcare do not have responsibilities for public health, all they can do is hope that those who do will take effective action, because there is no other action to prevent the increase in disease. Population ageing is a given fact, determined in part by the effectiveness of modern healthcare but determined much more by the fall in infant mortality in previous decades. Governments can attempt to control the growth of new technology by refusing to fund research and development, but that would have little effect because the major funder of new technology is now industry, not government.

Increasing demand

The demand for healthcare is also increasing as a result of a general trend called consumerism, fuelled by the Internet. The Venn diagram in Figure 1.2 shows that these drivers are inter-related, for example:

- Some of the new technology reduces the risk of surgical intervention and allows older people who would not have been considered fit for operation in the past to be treated; this also increases the need for healthcare.
- Attitudes are different. Now neither older people nor clinicians are willing to accept health problems as being caused by 'old age', and rightly so. The expectation of both is that people with health problems who ask for help should

have the same opportunity for diagnosis and treatment, whatever their age. This increases the demand for healthcare.

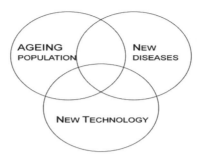

Figure 1.2 The drivers of demand

Managing demand

Managing demand is not easy but some steps can be taken, for example:

- Be very clear and explicit about the sub-groups of patients most likely to benefit from an intervention and, as a corollary, those who are least likely to benefit; payers also need to be explicit about healthcare conditions which will or will not be given treatment from publicly funded health services. These might include gender reassignment operations, symptomless inguinal hernia, aesthetic surgery, symptomless varicose veins, and symptomless gallstones. In addition, services may make explicit the decisions not to provide interventions which they deem to be of low value, such as intensive in-patient treatment for addiction, and operative repair of cruciate ligaments of the knee except for active sportsmen and women. A case can be made on the grounds of effectiveness for all these treatments, but management of demand is not possible if left to individual clinicians faced with the distress of the individual patient, and funders have to make decisions at a population level;

- Express the probability of benefit in absolute terms rather than relative terms, because the use of absolute rather than relative risk to communicate the benefits and harms almost always reduces the demand for care. For this reason evangelists for a new service usually express the benefits in relative rather than absolute terms, to gain an effect known as 'framing';

- Ensure that patients are given information about the risks and limitations of interventions as well as the benefits, for example when considering palliative chemotherapy.

These steps can be incorporated into patient decision aids, part of an effective patient engagement strategy. (2) One of the effects of widespread diffusion of the view of medical progress, influenced strongly by what has been called 'optimism bias', is that the public are keen for treatment. One of the benefits of promoting evidence-based patient choice, in which patients are given high quality information about benefits, risks and limitations, is to counteract optimism bias and reduce demand.

Managing clinical demand

> *There is a fashion in operations, as there is in sleeves and skirts: the triumph of some surgeon who has at last found out how to make a once desperate operation fairly safe is usually followed by a rage for that operation not only among the doctors, but actually among their patients.'* George Bernard Shaw (1906) Preface to *The Doctor's Dilemma.*

Demand is generated as often by clinicians as by patients. In its most overt form, clinician enthusiasm can contribute to the development of epidemics such as the false memory syndrome. Enthusiastic medical professions, altruistic and keen to do good, armed with information provided by enthusiastic promoters of new technology, and expressed in terms of relative benefit rather than absolute benefit, are, not surprisingly, the people who fuel the growth in demand. Clinical demand may be overtly expressed, for example by clinicians leading a campaign for a new service or a new facility such as a PET scanner or there may just be what is called 'creep', an inexorable increase in testing and treatment. Sometimes, science is put into practice by a well-considered national policy decision – for example, the introduction in the UK of breast cancer screening. However, many innovations are introduced into clinical practice by clinicians, who then seek the resources to fund the innovation from those who pay for the service. The ways in which changes or innovations in clinical practice increase the cost of care are manifold (see Table 1.1).

Table 1.1: How Innovations In Clinical Practice Increase Costs
• Treating conditions that were previously untreatable.
• Treating people who would previously have been untreated because of changing professional perceptions of need and appropriateness and changing public expectations. These may result from:
o Increasing safety of intervention;
o More acceptable, less invasive interventions;
o Changing attitudes to old age as a reason for refusing treatment;
o Changing expectations about health and disease amongst older people.
• Providing more expensive types of treatment:
o More expensive drugs;
o More expensive imaging;
o More expensive tests;
o More expensive staff.
• More intensive clinical practice:
o Longer duration of stay;
o More tests per patient;
o More professional interventions per patient;
o More treatments per patient.

Source: Gray, J.A.M., *Evidence-Based Healthcare* (3)

Innovation needs to decrease cost as well as increase it and there is now a drive to innovate for better value, harnessing the power of new technology and new ways of organising services. (4)

A classic study by Eddy in the USA (5) showed that, in a healthcare system in which expenditure is not finite, changes in the 'volume and intensity' of clinical practice are the main factors driving increases in the cost of care that can be controlled by those who pay for or manage healthcare. The other causes of increasing costs – population ageing, medical and general price inflation – are beyond the power of health service managers to control (Figure 1.3).

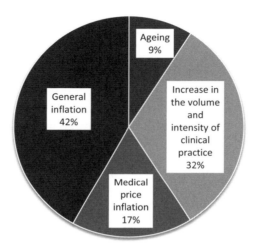

Figure 1.3 The causes of cost inflation

Managing innovation usually focuses on a small number of potentially high-cost interventions, for example the number of MRI machines. However, the conclusion from David Eddy's work, which is as true today as when it was published, is that every innovation, no matter how small, needs to have its introduction to, or removal from, the healthcare system carefully managed, particularly if it is for a common disease. The proposal that a screening test be introduced to the adult population would mean that, even if the test cost only £1 to administer, the total cost in the UK would be about £20 million. Even the administrative consequences of a simple test could amount to £2 million, and if a percentage of the population required further investigation the additional bill for a simple procedure could easily double, even if there were no clear evidence of added value.

Sustainable healthcare

Although need and demand will continue to grow, it is unlikely that resources will be invested in healthcare in the next decade at the rate at which they were invested in the last fifty years. A good working assumption when discussing resources with clinicians is to emphasise that 'there is no more money'.

20th century healthcare is an unsustainable model, both financially and from a carbon perspective, and the NHS has set a carbon reduction strategy that is as dramatic visually as it is numerically – a 10% reduction in 2007 carbon use by 2015, a 26% reduction by 2020 and a 50% reduction by 2050.

The good news for healthcare decision-makers is expressed in the title of the NHS strategy *Reducing Carbon, Improving Health* – namely, reducing carbon not only releases cash, it also improves the health of individuals and populations.

Welcome to the Third Healthcare Revolution

When a revolution is brewing, those in power are often the last to know, particularly if the weaponry of the revolution is knowledge and not gunpowder, if the artillery is the Web and not cannons, and if the revolutionaries are the patients, still mostly deferential and polite in the consultation. The Third Healthcare Revolution is now well under way and it will be as significant as the First and Second Revolutions.

Like the first Industrial Revolution, the First Healthcare Revolution was based on common sense. It was common sense that led to the invention of spinning and weaving machines (6) and it was common sense that led to the separation of water from sewage, long before microbiologists discovered the bacteria that caused cholera and typhoid (7). The Second Healthcare Revolution in both industry and healthcare was driven by science – chemists, engineers and physicists, who developed not only planes and plastics but also chemotherapy, transplants and artificial hips. The Second Healthcare Revolution led to dramatic improvements in the effectiveness of care but five problems remain and will not be solved by further scientific advances:

- failure to prevent the preventable;
- poor patient safety;
- variations in quality;
- waste of resources;
- inequalities in access and outcome.

The Third Industrial Revolution is transforming every service and industry and its drivers are knowledge, the World Wide Web, and citizens. Healthcare is relatively protected at present because of the need to deliver much of the care that people require in or near their own homes, but the job of both the clinician and the patient will be changed by the forces of the Revolution as dramatically as have the jobs of the investment banker and travel agent. This Revolution, driven by citizens, information technology and knowledge, is already underway to create new health services that:

- have the patient at their centre;
- are safer and more effective;
- produce greater value from the resources invested.

The impact of information technology (IT) is underestimated by many people who pay for or manage health services and who limit its influence to a separate domain called 'telemedicine' or 'eHealth' but IT will have as big an influence in 21st century health as pharmaceuticals had in the 20th century. Google, Microsoft, Cisco, IBM and the other giants will be as influential as Big Pharma is today. It is important to remember that when Tim Berners-Lee was asked his ambition for 2010 in the millennium copy of *Wired,* he replied that it was that 'no-one would use the term Internet in 2010'. The thing we call the Internet will change forever the prevention of disease, the promotion of health and the way we pay for and manage healthcare.

Questions for reflection when teaching or developing networks

If using these in network building or teaching, give one of the questions to the group and ask them to work in pairs to reflect on the question for three minutes; try to get people who do not know one another to work together.

When taking feedback, let each pair make only one point. In the interests of equity, if you start with the pair on the left-hand side of the room for the first question, start with the pair on the right-hand side of the room for the second question.

- What three steps would you take to reduce the demand for healthcare?
- How could the Internet be used to help health services cope with the challenges they face?
- What technological innovations could reduce the cost of healthcare?
- What technological innovations could reduce the need for healthcare?
- What technological innovations could reduce the demand for healthcare?

References

(1)   Showalter, E. (1997) *Hystories: Hysterical Epidemics and Modern Culture.* Columbia University Press.

(2)   Gray, J.A.M. (2005) *The Resourceful Patient.* eRosetta Press.

(3)   Gray, J.A.M. (2005) *Evidence-Based Healthcare.* Elsevier.

(4)   Christensen, C.M, Grossman, J.H. and Hwang, J. (2008) *The Innovator's Prescription: a Disruptive Solution for Health Care.* McGraw-Hill.

(5)   Eddy, D.M. (1993) Three Battles To Watch In The 1990s. *JAMA* 270: 520-6.

(6)   White Jr., L. (1962) *Medieval Technology and Social Change* Oxford University Press

(7)   Castells, M. (1996) *The Rise of the Network Society: The Information Age, Economy, Society and Culture.* Blackwell.

2

THE MEANINGS OF VALUE

This chapter will:

- demonstrate the subjective nature of value;
- clarify the different meanings of the term 'value';
- show how the meaning of the term can be explained in both words and numbers;
- introduce the concept of public value.

By the end of this chapter you will have an understanding of:

- the difference between the moral meaning of the term 'value' and its economic meaning;
- how to define the economic meaning of the term 'value' from the perspective of clinicians and patients, and the perspective of those who invest in healthcare or manage it;
- how to help a management or clinical team reach agreement on the way in which they will use the term 'value'.

'Oh fuck!' said the surgeon, gazing at the liver newly exposed by his generous incision from the sternum to the umbilicus.

Human liver looks like calves' liver or lamb's liver – smooth, firm, shiny, and cerise. The human liver is a large organ. It lies just below the rib cage with a large lobe on the right side tapering to a left lobe which lies across the midline. The liver is a generous organ. It has more capacity than is needed and good health is possible even if half the liver is destroyed or removed. The liver is a bloody organ. The large amount of blood that flows through the liver means that cancer cells often lodge and grow in the liver to become metastases, and these 'liver secondaries' were regarded as a death sentence until advances in surgery and anaesthesia enabled surgical treatment, and perhaps cure, if the secondaries were situated in the left lobe of the liver which can be detached from the right, main lobe and removed. Ten days before surgery, x-rays had found secondaries only in the left lobe of the liver, but when the liver lay exposed under the merciless theatre lights, little white specks covered the surface of the right lobe and the left lobe; surgical treatment would therefore be futile.

'Oh, fuck!' said the surgeon and, after a pause, 'Let's go ahead anyway.'

Four perspectives

Different people have different perspectives:

The trainee's perspective

That Catholics enjoyed themselves on Sundays was a cause of universal disapproval to Scottish Presbyterians in the nineteen-seventies, and a cause of envy to not a few. After Mass, Catholics could relax and enjoy themselves, although in a Scottish city in those days the opportunities for enjoyment on the Sabbath were few. The young doctor, who had spent seven hours on the liver operation, and kept watch in the evening on the patient's post-operative course, received no extra pay. There was no direct cost to him, but, even in Scotland, he could have spent the day going to church, playing golf, sleeping, or studying.

The opportunity cost was high but he regarded it as negligible, both at the time and in retrospect, because his frustration at this experience was one of the reasons that he decided to leave surgery, a move of great value to himself and to those future patients who would have undeniably received poor quality care from an academic surgeon whose strengths and weaknesses were better suited to a career in public health.

The payer's and manager's perspective

The perspective of the hospital management and the payer, the local NHS Board, are not recorded because they never knew the operation was taking place. The theatre that was used was available for emergencies and some direct costs were entailed, swabs and sutures, for example, but the staff would have spent the day on cleaning and maintenance, or reading the ubiquitous *Sunday Post*, had the operation not appeared on the theatre list; no other operation had to be postponed or delayed as a consequence. Had they known it was happening, the manager and the payer might have viewed it as a worthwhile investment, although it is to be hoped that they would have classified it as a futile investment of resources had they appreciated the significance of the secondaries in the right-hand lobe of the liver. If the right-hand lobe of the liver had been clear of secondaries, the operation, the first of its kind in that hospital, would almost certainly have been classified as progress, and progress has both cost and value.

The development of new skills within a hospital or health service not only allows it to improve the health of the population it serves but also allows it to attract more patients, increase the hospital income, and allow further capital investment and staff recruitment.

The surgeon's perspective

From the surgeon's perspective, the operation was valuable. The exposure and ligation of the left hepatic artery and vein, the preservation of the common bile duct, and the satisfactory sealing of the large exposed surface of the liver from which the left lobe had been sliced off, had all gone well. The condition of the patient was satisfactory during and after surgery. The presence of the secondaries in the right lobe was to be regretted. The operation was not curative but others would be: the surgeon had now done a hemi-hepatectomy. This operation is now a standard procedure and he, like other surgeons, performed many of them with success, but progress has to start somewhere. There has to be a first patient to be given penicillin or have a heart transplant, and for each surgeon there has to be a first.

In a brave series of papers, a respected cardiac surgeon reported how mortality increased temporarily when he changed his technique before falling to levels much lower than with his old technique. Progress has a price as well as a reward.

The patient's perspective

The perspective of the patient, although not on record, would depend both upon what she was told, and her personal values. She probably valued the operation highly, because many patients appreciate the fact that their clinicians are trying everything that can be done to beat cancer. Even if she had been told that there were secondaries left behind, at least some had been cut out, and for some patients that would have been of high value. It may have been that the secondaries left in the right lobe would have lain quiet for years. Such a possibility, remote though it is, cannot be dismissed.

The meanings and definitions of value

The payer's value

From the perspective of payers for healthcare, whose responsibility it is to allocate money among different groups of patients, and, if the government is the payer, different jurisdictions, value is at its maximum when it is impossible to increase the good by reallocating a single pound or euro from one group of patients to another, or from one part of the country to another.

The patient's value

From the perspective of the patient, the value of the care received is measured not just by the outcome of the care they receive, but by the way it is delivered. The value that patients place on the service they have received will be reduced if, for example, they feel that:

- their time has been wasted waiting in a clinic for a consultation at which laboratory results were unavailable;
- they were treated rudely and impersonally;
- they did not receive as much information as they wished.

Even if the patient is not paying directly, their valuation of the service is of central importance. Good outcomes are necessary but not sufficient; good patient experience will also be of essential importance to the 21st century patient, and therefore, to those who provide and pay for their care.

The clinician's value

Busy clinicians highly value the opportunity to use their time, their scarcest resource, to see those patients most likely to benefit from their skill, and to provide for each patient the best care that patient needs quickly and easily. Most clinicians now accept that 'best' means the best that can be provided by the service in which they are working. This may be different from everything that is possible for a particular patient were costs not a consideration. The clinician in a world in which resources were limitless might try treatments which could give hope, and which might work for one in a million patients. However, when working in a system in which payers have to derive maximum value for the whole population for which they are responsible, treatments with this level of benefit – the offer of hope combined with a one in a million chance of success – is of too low a value to be acceptable, and would therefore not be included in the range of treatment options available to the clinician working in the service. Not all clinicians find this tension easy to bear but this dual responsibility to the individual patient and the population will become part of professional practice.

The manager's value

The meaning of 'value' to a manager is akin to that of the payer because managers are responsible for groups of patients, not individuals. They want the care to be effective and safe for the individual in order to minimise complaints, which are time-consuming and bad for morale, and errors, which can be expensive for the organisation; but most of all the manager wants productivity.

The manager of a healthcare facility such as a hospital is rarely told by the payer how much to invest for each patient group. She may be told to invest in a service where there are obvious deficiencies, usually manifest by long waiting times. A manager has to allocate resources into three main types of spend – direct clinical care, clinical support services such as biochemistry, and management.

The management team of a health service also has to decide which services should get more money, or, in times of retrenchment, which should get less. The manager of a health service values most her ability to deliver care of a standard that will maximise the possibility of benefit and minimise the possibility of harm, while satisfying their payers' requirements. The scarcest resource for a manager is freedom of action.

Industry's value

Although it is common to talk about the healthcare industry, healthcare is a service although it does, however, stimulate and support pharmaceutical, equipment, diagnostic and IT industries.

Frequently industrial developers of new products or services are disappointed by the lack of enthusiasm generated by their latest product or service. The reason for this is not simply the added cost that the new technology will require, at least in the short term, but the failure to appreciate the different meanings of the term 'value', complicated by the fact that many health services are so hard-pressed financially that they are unable to create a fund, sometimes called an 'invest-to-save' fund, that would allow the necessary investment in the short term to increase value in the long term.

Public value

The public, the population paying for and served by a health service, have to decide how much they want to invest in healthcare rather than defence or education or other budgets. They also have to make decisions between the short and the long term and, as the disasters that will result from climate change come ever closer, the health service will need to recognise that the public will expect them not only to add value by making the population healthier by the healthcare they provide, but also to minimise and mitigate the impact of health services on the environment.

Dictionary definitions of value

There are two types of dictionary. The first is that which gives only the definition of the lexicographer who wrote it, like Dr Johnson's dictionary. The second type of dictionary, requiring massively more resources at a level not available to Dr Johnson, gives not only the lexicographer's definition but also examples of the word in use. For instance, the *Shorter Oxford English Dictionary* clearly distinguishes between two different meanings of the word 'value', both in common use in healthcare.

One meaning of the word 'value' may be described as its moral meaning, namely 'the status of a thing or the estimate in which it is held according to its real or supposed worth, usefulness, or importance', the definition from the late Middle English. This use of the word 'value' is common in healthcare, for example, the hospital which claims that 'we value patient choice', or 'we value openness and honesty'.

The second meaning in the *Shorter Oxford English Dictionary* can be described as the economic meaning, and one of the four variants that the *Shorter Oxford English Dictionary* gives is 'that amount of some commodity, medium of exchange, etc. which is considered to be an equivalent for something else', and it gives as an example the meaning of the term in use in 1806, *'we could hardly be said to have value for our money'*. In the specialised *Dictionary of Health Economics*, published by Anthony Culyer in 2005 (1), the author, acting as lexicographer, defines value by saying that *'in economics, value is usually taken as a maximum amount that an individual or group is willing to pay for a particular good or service rather than go without it.'* He also defines 'marginal value' as *'the value of marginal benefit: the maximum an individual is willing to pay for an increment of benefit'*. The best shorthand definition of value is to describe it as the relationship between outcome and cost, expressed as the net health benefit – the difference between benefit and harm, taking into account the resources used.

The word 'value' is now widely used in medical literature, but if one searches for 'value' one finds articles which relate not only to words but also, mercifully, to numbers.

Numerical definitions of value

The Vienna School of Philosophy flourished in the 1920s and 1930s and became very influential in Britain, where it gave rise to what is known as 'logical positivism'. Their leading light in Britain was A.J. Ayer, whose book *Language, Truth and Logic* (2), published in 1935 when he was 24, had a massive impact. The logical positivists took an approach to definition of the meaning of a term that did not rely on words alone. In his book, Ayer said that:

> *Instead of trying to understand the meaning of a proposition by analysing the meaning of the individual words that compose it, another approach should be taken. The criterion which we use to test the genuineness of apparent statements of facts is the criterion of verifiability. We say that a sentence is factually significant to any given person if, and only if, he knows how to verify the proposition which it purports to express – that is, if he knows what observations will lead him, under certain conditions, to accept the proposition as being true, or reject it as being false. And with regard to questions, the procedure is the same. We enquire in every case what observations will lead us to answer the question one way or the other, and, if none can be discovered, we must conclude that the sentence under consideration does not, as far as we are concerned, express a genuine question, however strongly its grammatical appearance may suggest that it does.*

An example of numerical expressions of value which would have pleased A. J. Ayer is set out below:

> *Alternating pressure mattresses were associated with lower overall costs (£283.06 per patient on average, 95% confidence interval £377.59 to £976.79) mainly due to reduced lengths of stay in hospital and greater benefits (a delay in time to ulceration of 10.64 days on average, 24.40 to 3.09).* (3)

For many years, the benefits of healthcare interventions were measured in terms of the numbers of years of life added. The use of the number of years of life gained as the criterion used to assess new, or existing, healthcare interventions led to a focus on length of life as the aim of healthcare, with priority being given to research on, and subsequent investment in services for, 'killer diseases'.

A key paper was published in 1978 by Rosser and Kind called A Scale of Valuations of States of Illness: Is There a Social Consensus? (4) This paper was of immense importance and led to the development of a measure called the quality adjusted life year (QALY), which is a measure of health-related quality of life, taking into account both quantity and quality. A year of perfect health was deemed to be worth 1, death was usually given 0, although society agrees that there are some situations that could be regarded as worse than death and which need negative numbers.

People who had, or people who looked after people who had, chronic disabling diseases that did not significantly affect the length of life, such as depression, argued that this approach discriminated against disabling diseases, and as a consequence steps were taken to develop measurements that would take into account quality of life as well as quantity.

The development of the Disability Adjusted Life Year (DALY) has also been of great importance for policy-makers, and in the 1996 publication *The Global Burden of Disease* (5), the World Health Organisation included quality adjusted measures as well as mortality in a significant review of previous thinking on healthcare priorities. This major work, edited by Murray and Lopez, significantly changed the ranking of diseases and brought mental health problems much higher up the league table of human suffering.

Reaching agreement on meaning

Because there are multiple meanings and definitions, it is essential to reach agreement on how the term 'value' will be used before starting a discussion at a meeting. In every meeting in which value is to be discussed, either implicitly or explicitly, it is essential to reach agreement on a single meaning that can be used, if only for the duration of the meeting. Here is how to do that:

- Prepare copies of the definition you want to use, or have it as a PowerPoint. *The Shorter Oxford English Dictionary* definition is good for most purposes, namely 'that amount of some commodity, medium of exchange, etc. which is considered to be an equivalent for something else'. It is also helpful to type the example of the meaning of the term in use in 1806, 'we could hardly be said to have value for our money', and to emphasise that it is the relationship between outcome and cost.

- If you have time you can let the group come to the conclusion that there are two different types of meaning, the moral meaning and the economic meaning, but in most meetings there is not time for this and you should tell the group that they should focus on the economic meaning.

- Ask people to work in pairs and give them two minutes, no more, to agree on words that come to mind when they think of the value derived from resources invested in health services; tell them to remember that value is different from quality.

- Take feedback with one word from each pair and write them on a flipchart.   If possible, they should come close to *The Shorter Oxford English Dictionary* definition which can then be revealed.   However, it is best to reveal this after the group has done its work.

Questions for reflection when teaching or developing networks

If using these in network building or teaching, give one of the questions to the group and ask them to work in pairs to reflect on the question for three minutes; try to get people who do not know one another to work together.

When taking feedback, let each pair make only one point. In the interests of equity, if you start with the pair on the left-hand side of the room for the first question, start with the pair on the right-hand side of the room for the second question.

- Is it possible for those who pay for and those who manage healthcare to reach agreement on the meaning of value?
- Is it possible for a clinician to be more concerned about the consequences of their decisions about an individual patient for the whole population without behaving unethically towards the patient?
- If you were the Chief Executive of a big pharmaceutical company, how would you assess the value of a new drug?
- Can you identify a service which has passed the point of optimality, or will do so if growth is not slowed or stopped?
- How would you explain that 'more is not necessarily better' if you were given 2 minutes on local radio?

References

(1)   Culyer, A. (2005) *Dictionary of Health Economics*. Edward Elgar Publishing.

(2)   Ayer, A.J. (1936) *Language, Truth And Logic*. Gollancz.

(3)   Iglesias et al (2006) Pressure Relieving Support Surfaces (PRESSURE) Trial: Cost-effectiveness Analysis. *BMJ* 332: 1416-1418.

(4)   Rosser, R. and Kind, P. (1978) A Scale of Valuations of States of Illness: Is there a Social Consensus? *Internat. J. Epidemiol.* 7: 347-358.

(5)   Murray, C.J.L. and Lopez, A.D. (1996) *The Global Burden of Disease.* WHO, Geneva.

3

THE BEST RESPONSE TO 21st CENTURY CHALLENGES

This chapter will:

- set out the principal economic terms used in decision-making;
- review how the relative importance of different terms changes over time;
- introduce the concept of optimality.

By the end of this chapter you will have an understanding of:

- the distinction between efficacy, effectiveness and efficiency;
- the different meanings of cost-benefit, cost-utility and cost-effectiveness assessment;
- the relationship between resources invested and the benefit and harm that results;
- how to help people understand the concept of optimality.

The crisis that we face will not be solved by more science or more money, and, even if there were more money, carbon will be the key constraint. What is needed are new systems for making decisions and managing care and a new culture that is focused on patients, and with a hatred of waste. A new culture requires good leadership but it also requires a common language and a common set of concepts on which to base decisions and manage care.

Effectiveness and efficiency

In the last three decades of the 20th century, health service payers and managers were appropriately preoccupied with effectiveness and efficiency, and only services that did more good than harm, at reasonable cost, were considered for funding.

However, of developed countries, only the United Kingdom faced serious resource constraints in the 1980s and was forced to think about opportunity costs rather than simply taking new interventions which had a favourable result from cost-benefit or cost-effectiveness analyses. Since then, every other major developed economy, which is committed to offering healthcare to its whole population, has had to face up to limits placed on healthcare spending. In Germany, Japan, and Italy, for example, evidence-based decision-making has become much more explicit. The United States remains an exception but President Obama is determined to end that.

It was in the United Kingdom, therefore, that the response to the work of Archie Cochrane was most enthusiastic.

> *He lived and died, a severe porphyric, who smoked too much, without the consolation of a wife, a religious belief, or a merit award, but he didn't do too badly.*

These were the words of Archie Cochrane when he wrote his own obituary for the *British Medical Journal*. As befits the man, they were ironic, clear, accurate, and understated.   Few people had more influence on healthcare in the last fifty years of the 20th century than Archie Cochrane, firstly, by his insistence on the importance of the randomised controlled trial, secondly, by his challenge to the medical and research establishments that they should organise all of their knowledge properly, leading to the creation of the Cochrane Collaboration, and, thirdly, by the publication of his *Random Reflections on Health Services* with the title *Effectiveness and Efficiency*. (1) This small book was published in 1972 and the focus of 20th century healthcare became effectiveness and efficiency.

The era of effectiveness

> *All effective treatments must be free.*

This, wrote Cochrane, was the device his banner carried at a Communist rally in the 1930s, written after considerable thought but making no impact on the communists on the march. But it did make an impact on Cochrane, who remained obsessed with the need for treatments to be demonstrated to be effective and then, if they were, for those treatments to be made available through a National Health Service. For Cochrane it was clear that the single best method for demonstrating the effectiveness of a treatment was the randomised controlled clinical trial, and he promoted the importance of the trial with commitment, energy, intelligence, and a considerable degree of cunning throughout the rest of his professional career. As a result, the term 'effectiveness' entered the general vocabulary not only of the research worker but of all those who manage and pay for healthcare.

After thirty-five years in common use, the term 'effective', inevitably, is now used much more loosely, and has many different meanings. Some people still use it with the original meaning. For some clinicians, however, 'effective' is used to mean that, in their experience, patients appear to have got better, or even that a single patient got better while using the treatment.

Defining ineffectiveness

The people who argued most strongly for the need for Cochrane's definition of effectiveness to be adopted also pointed out that absence of evidence of effectiveness is not proof of absence of effect. This allows people to argue that the absence of evidence of beneficial effect in, for example, breast cancer screening for women under the age of 50, was simply due to the fact that the trials that had been organised were too small, and that the proposition that 'screening for breast cancer in women under 50 is ineffective' was simply a statement of effectiveness according to the rules laid down by those who funded research and healthcare. There is some truth in this accusation.

Another reason why the term 'effective' fell into disrepute was that treatments have both good and bad effects, but the word 'effective' had come to be synonymous with good effects, reflecting in part the problems of positive publication bias. This has encouraged researchers and editors to publish articles which not only emphasise the size of the beneficial effects of new treatments, a phenomenon called positive publication bias, but ignores the potential harms of treatments, a phenomenon known as optimism bias. (2)

The limitations of 'effectiveness'

For these reasons, the term 'effective' is no longer useful as a means of sharply distinguishing 'the effective' from 'the ineffective'. Instead of the shorthand term 'effective', therefore, it has become common to talk about the balance between good and harm, for example by describing the results of research in terms of both benefits and harms. Some interventions, such as prostate cancer screening, have weak evidence of benefit and strong evidence of harm, whereas other treatments, such as statins, have strong evidence of considerable benefit with strong evidence that harm is uncommon. Furthermore, we are far beyond the era in which 'all effective treatments must be free', and in every society there are examples of 'effective' treatments, if we wish to continue using that term, which cannot be afforded for the whole population.

It is certainly necessary to demonstrate that a new screening programme, diagnostic test, or treatment, does more good than harm by good quality research, preferably based on a systematic review of all existing research. However, that by itself is no longer a guarantee of funding. In an attempt to resolve this problem, governments and payers have had increasingly to turn to Archie Cochrane's second great legacy – efficiency – as the criterion by which interventions should be judged.

The era of efficiency and productivity

The multiple meanings of the term 'efficiency' illustrate Wittgenstein's principle that arguments result from a failure of the parties concerned to agree on the meaning of the terms they are using. (3) Two people can have a furious argument about whether or not a health service is efficient, when one is in fact talking about cost-effectiveness and the other about productivity, two of the commonly used meanings of efficiency.

The productivity of a health service relates the inputs to the outputs, for example the number of cases per bed or the number of operations per surgeon. The efficiency or cost-effectiveness relates the outcomes to inputs, for example the number of people cured related to the operations carried out.

The limitations of 'efficiency'

The use of Quality Adjusted Life Years allows the cost and benefit of different services to be expressed in the same currency and this in turn allows services to be compared with both one another and with some threshold above which services are not regarded as 'cost-effective'. This approach has been very helpful and has been widely used, notably by NICE in the United Kingdom and by the Australian Drugs Reimbursement Committee. (4, 5)

However, even the use of this criterion does not solve all the problems of decision-makers, principally because most societies are now faced with the prospect of having more interventions which come within the threshold of cost-effectiveness than can be afforded by health services. As with effectiveness, efficiency is necessary but not sufficient. It is certainly important for every society to adopt some means of appraising the costs and benefits of interventions that clinicians or industry offer to them, but this will not solve all the problems, in part because of having more interventions that meet the criteria than can be afforded, in part because people with rare diseases may present very challenging problems to decision-makers.

The treatment a person with a rare disease requires often falls outside the threshold of cost-effectiveness but, if not funded, may result in the death of an individual, sometimes an individual whose name and image has become familiar to the public and to politicians. This is something society finds difficult to accept.

Optimality and value – key concepts for the 21st century

Avedis Donabedian was an Armenian, and his nationality was in many ways as important to him as were Cochrane's roots in Scotland. In 2003, Oxford University Press published a book whose copyright rested with the American University of Armenia entitled *An Introduction to Quality Assurance in Health Care* (8). In his preface, Donabedian states that: *'It was with great reluctance that I undertook to write this book'*, but from *'the happy state'* of his retirement, he felt he was recalled by *'the urgent need, insistently and repeatedly brought to my attention, for a brief, coherent account of quality assurance in health care for use by students of the subject in my native Armenia'.*

Donabedian wrote the book during the end stages of what his editor describes as *'combat with an avaricious cancer that weakened his musculature but left his mind untouched'*, and the book was published in the year 2000, three years after his death at the age of 81. The book is outstanding, only 200 pages long, but pulling together a lifetime's work of clear thinking. Donabedian's previous classic was his three volume *Explorations in Quality Assessment and Monitoring*, published in 1980 (9), and it was in this work that he described not only structure, process, and outcome but also his 'unifying model of benefit, risk and cost'. The power of this model is that it described for the first time the fact that as resources are increased in healthcare, benefit increases, but the increase in benefit then flattens off, illustrating what some people have called the law of diminishing returns (Figure 3.1).

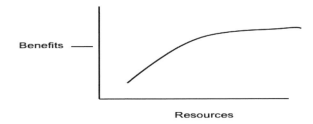

Benefits

Resources

Figure 3.1 The law of diminishing benefit

In contrast, the amount of harm done increases in direct proportion to the investment of resources. For each unit of increase in resource, there is a unit increase in the volume of care, and a unit increase in the amount of harm. In fact there may be a progressive increase in the amount of harm if, with each unit of increase in the availability of care, patients who are less fit and more at risk of harm are covered by the service (Figure 3.2)

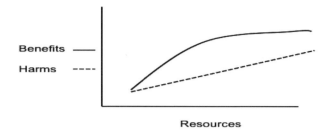

Resources

Figure 3.2 The law of undiminishing harm

As a consequence, there may come a point where the investment of additional resources will lead to a reduction in the net benefit, calculated by subtracting the harm from the benefit. Donabedian's prose is crystal clear:

> *If benefits to health are used as the sole criterion of quality, there is no clear-cut level of service which corresponds to optimum care. One must presumably continue to add services until no measurable additional benefits accrue, but that is to proceed without considering the risk that is inherent to a greater or lesser degree in all health care...the services prescribe the use first of large benefits and small risk. Then, as services are added, each increment has progressively larger risks and smaller benefits...the curve of 'benefits against risks' rises to a peak.*

In his last book, Donabedian describes optimality explicitly as:

> *The balancing of improvements in health against the cost of such improvements. The definition implies there is a 'best' or 'optimum relationship' between costs and benefits of health care, a point below which more benefits could be obtained at costs that are low relative to benefits and above which additional benefits are obtained at costs too large relative to corresponding benefits. (Figure 3.3)*

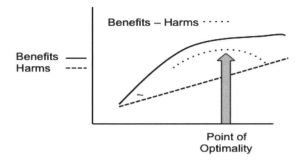

Figure 3.3 The optimal relationship between resources, benefit and harm

Clinicians and patient groups often desire maximally effective healthcare, but for those who pay for healthcare in a time in which need and demand are greater than the resources that are available, optimality is a more appropriate objective. When optimality is achieved, value is at a maximum. Patient groups can also appreciate optimality, provided that they are informed about the harms of treatment.

Economists' perspectives

This subject is of course meat and drink to economists and many have written on this issue, notably Kenneth Arrow, Alan Maynard, Alain Enthoven, Thomas Rice and Gavin Mooney. Their perspectives differ from one to another, and to that of the author of this book, which may be called the 'evidence based' perspective, which is not without its critics (8).

All are agreed, however, that resources are finite and difficult decisions have to be made about the allocation and use of these resources to reach the optimal point at which the maximum value is derived from the resources invested, whether those resources be measured in terms of professional time or money or, the key currency for the 21st century – carbon.

Although not focused on health services, the ideas of the two economists who were awarded the Nobel Prize for Economics in 2009, Oliver Williamson and Elinor Ostrom, are also very relevant.

Williamson's work has been on transaction costs, on the costs entailed in trying to specify and manage complex problems by the use of longer, tighter contracts, whether in a market or in a bureaucracy. The separation of payer from provider and the use of competition in a market, or audit and performance management in a bureaucracy, have benefits, but they also have costs and there can come a time when the costs are greater than the benefits and that time may have come in healthcare. The alternative is not inaction but the development of systems of care that involve patients in finding solutions to the challenges they face in a time of zero growth.

Elinor Ostrom has spent decades studying 'the tragedy of the commons' – how common wealth, forests or grazing land or fishing rights, can be destroyed if all the individuals who use them increase their use by an amount so small that it does not appear to make any difference. Her message of hope is that the tragedy is not inevitable, and that there are many examples where people acting together can preserve and increase the value of the common wealth. This is a message that clinicians and patients need to heed.

What has been equally important has been the involvement of big guns from the world of academic management studies, notably Michael Porter and Clayton Christensen. This interest, stimulated by the cost of healthcare in the United States and President Obama's determination to tackle inequity, has brought healthcare centre-stage, but their thinking and writing is equally relevant in other countries.

Questions for reflection when teaching or developing networks

If using these in network building or teaching, give one of the questions to the group and ask them to work in pairs to reflect on the question for three minutes; try to get people who do not know one another to work together.

When taking feedback, let each pair make only one point. In the interests of equity, if you start with the pair on the left-hand side of the room for the first question, start with the pair on the right-hand side of the room for the second question.

- How could a population be helped to understand that increasing the level of investment in a service might lead to a reduction in value for the population?
- Can you identify a service which has passed the point of optimality, or will do so if growth is not slowed or stopped?
- How would you explain the quotation 'more is not necessarily better' if you were given 2 minutes on local radio?

References

(1)   Cochrane, A. (1972) *Effectiveness & Efficiency: Random Reflections on Health Services.* Nuffield Press. (reprinted 2004, *RSM)*

(2)   Chalmers, I. and Matthews, R. (2006) What are the Implications of Optimism Bias in Clinical Research? *Lancet 367: 449-450.*

(3)   Kenny, A. (1994) *The Wittgenstein Reader.* Blackwell.

(4)   Pearson, S.D. and Rawlins, M.D. (2005) Quality, Innovation & Value for Money: NICE & The British National Health Service. *JAMA 294: 2618-2622.*

(5)   Henry, D.A. et al (2005) Drug Prices and Value for Money: The Australian Pharmaceutical Benefits Scheme. *JAMA 294: 2630-2632.*

---

(6)   Donabedian, A. (2002) *An Introduction to Quality Assurance in Health Care.* Oxford University Press.

(7)   Donabedian, A. (1980) *Explorations in Quality Assessment & Monitoring. (3 vols.)* Health Administration Press.

(8)   Kristiansen, I.S. and Mooney, G. (2006) *Evidence-based Medicine: In its Place.* Routledge.

4

THE TOP TEN QUESTIONS ABOUT VALUE

To increase value, those who pay for and manage healthcare, including the hundreds of thousands of clinicians worldwide who manage resources as well as looking after individual patients, have to ask ten questions.

(1) How much money should we spend on healthcare?

When this is answered, the next question is:

(2) Is the money allocated for the infrastructure that supports clinical care at a level which will maximise value?

When this is answered, the next question is:

(3) Have we distributed the money for clinical care to different parts of the country by a method that recognises both variation in need and maximises value for the whole population?

When this is answered, the next question is:

(4) Has money been distributed to different patient groups by decision-making that is not only equitable but also maximises value for the whole population?

When resources have been allocated to a service for a particular group of patients, two further questions have to be asked about the service offered:

(5) Are all the interventions offered likely to confer a good balance of benefit and harm, at an affordable cost, for this group of patients?

(6) Are the patients most likely to benefit from the interventions, and least likely to be harmed by them, clearly defined?

Finally, having allocated the money to a service manager, four questions have to be asked about the use of resources:

(7) Is effectiveness being maximised?

(8) Are the risks of care being minimised?

(9) Can costs be reduced further without increasing harm or reducing benefit?

(10) Could each patient's experience be improved?

Those who pay for and those who manage healthcare are interested in all these questions. Traditionally the lead is taken by payers for the earlier questions and by those who have direct management responsibility for the later questions, with both parties interested in all of them.

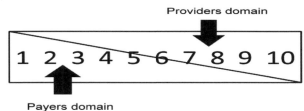

Figure 4.1 The 20th century relationship between providers and payers

As pressure increases there is a convergence of interests. On the one hand, those who provide care and patient groups are increasingly involved in lobbying for more resources for healthcare. On the other hand, those who pay for healthcare are increasingly involved in assuring and ensuring the quality of care provided through 'pay-for-performance' requirements in their contracts.

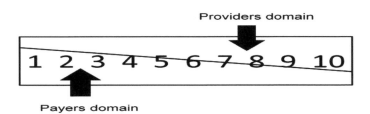

Figure 4.2 The 21st century relationship between providers and payers

These questions, and some answers, form the next part of this book.

Question 1: How much money should we spend on healthcare?

> **This section will:**
>
> - examine the choices faced by a Treasury or Government which has to consider investment in healthcare in competition with all other bids for public sector funding;
> - review the different aspects of this choice, depending upon the way in which healthcare is funded.
>
> **By the end of this section you will have an understanding of:**
>
> - the arguments against increasing investment in healthcare;
> - the irrelevance of insurance-based systems as a means of increasing the proportion of GNP spent on healthcare.

There appears to be no limit to the amount of money that can be spent on healthcare. Everyone could have his own personal physician and still want a second opinion. The record is currently held by the United States, which spends more on healthcare, as a proportion of Gross National Product (GNP) and in terms of dollars per head, than any other large developed country.

One view is that it does not matter how much of the GNP is spent on healthcare because people might as well spend money on health as on holidays or cars or any other type of conspicuous consumption. It does, however, depend on how the money is raised. If, as in the US, healthcare insurance is part of the employment costs, the increasing cost of insurance affects the costs of American goods and contributes to other economic problems.

The amount that is spent on healthcare is a value judgement based on a number of different criteria, for example:

- The proportion of the GNP spent on healthcare in other comparable countries. Comparison with spending in the European Union was an important factor in influencing the

Labour government to spend a higher proportion of the UK GNP on health.

- Consideration of the opportunity costs of increasing spending on healthcare in comparison with all the other demands on government funds, for example education, defence or law enforcement. Every pound or euro spent on healthcare is a pound or euro that cannot be spent on education, and that is a value decision.

- The relationship between the capacity of the service and public concern about service shortfall. Concern about waiting times, for example, has driven many countries to increase investment in healthcare, but this type of decision-making may simply lead to a diversion of resources to the particular service highlighted by the media, rather than increasing the amount of GNP allocated to healthcare. The evidence for this approach is weak and one well conducted study found that 'despite more resources physicians in regions of high healthcare intensity did not report greater ease in obtaining needed services or providing high quality care'. (1)

This debate involves macro-economic decisions. In countries like the UK, in which expenditure is either public or private, the decision for those who distribute the public purse is relatively simple, based firstly on a decision about the proportion of the GNP that is to be public expenditure and then the proportion of that expenditure that is to be allocated to healthcare. In many of those countries in which the proportion of the GNP spent on healthcare is greater than 10%, the options are more complex, because much of this spending is not from private citizens making a decision to invest in healthcare rather than another holiday, but from insurance schemes subsidised or underwritten by government, and this affects the size of public sector spending.

Where insurance schemes are not supported by public sector spending, they are usually supported by employers, and this affects the price of goods and services produced by the country. In the 1970s, the cost of healthcare insurance became greater than the cost of steel in

Chrysler cars. This was not the only problem faced by Chrysler; the quality of their cars was much worse than the quality of Japanese cars, but the combination of cost and quality dealt a heavy blow to Chrysler and to all American car companies.

Many economists believe that both increases in public sector spending, and increases in the cost of goods and services because of health insurance cost increases, harm the economy of a country and, therefore, in the long-term will impair the health of its population. A Treasury, therefore, can argue that it is of greater value to the health of a population to control investment in healthcare than to let it run uncontrolled. In most developed countries the Finance Ministry or Treasury, and not the Health Ministry, has decided that not much more than 10% of the GNP should be spent on healthcare.

Following the economic earthquake of 2008 and 2009, most governments in Europe have cut back on public expenditure, with the United Kingdom government specifying that the NHS would be exempt from the swingeing budget cuts, stating in the White Paper *Equity and Excellence: Liberating the NHS*, published in July 2010, an explicit commitment 'that we will increase healthcare spending in real terms in each year of the Parliament'. However, it seems unlikely that many governments will invest heavily in healthcare in the next decade.

Questions for reflection when teaching or developing networks

If using these in network building or teaching, give one of the questions to the group and ask them to work in pairs to reflect on the question for three minutes; try to get people who do not know one another to work together.

When taking feedback, let each pair make only one point. In the interests of equity, if you start with the pair on the left-hand side of the room for the first question, start with the pair on the right-hand side of the room for the second question.

- What is the evidence that investment in public services other than healthcare would have a greater benefit on the health of the population than increased investment in healthcare?
- What might happen if people in their twenties were allowed to opt out of patient for the health service?
- What, if any, are the benefits of funding healthcare by insurance rather than taxes, if insurance funding is not able to increase the proportion of national wealth invested in healthcare because of the impact that higher insurance premiums would have on industry?

Reference

(1)   Sirovich, B. et al (2006) Regional Variations on Health Care Intensity and Physician Perceptions of Quality of Care. *Ann. Int. Med.* 144: 641-649.

Question 2: Is the money allocated for the infrastructure that supports clinical care at a level which will maximise value?

This section will:

- review the principal expenditures which do not directly serve the needs of patients;
- examine the arguments used to justify the investment of top-sliced activities in terms of the value produced;
- explain the problems encountered when trying to measure the value of those activities.

By the end of this section you will have an understanding of:

- the reasons why health service funds should be invested in research;
- the difficulty in deciding how much investment in information technology adds value and in determining when investment should stop;
- explain why a health service should invest in the education of the professionals it needs;
- justify some investment in management and the arguments used to determine the proportion of resources that should be invested.

Eyeball to eyeball, clinician and patient: the consultation is at the heart of the patient's experience of healthcare. About 40,000 consultations occur every day in a population of one million and many decisions are reached in the consultation by the two protagonists or partners. Many clinicians also make decisions without directly engaging with the patient, either by providing knowledge from their laboratory or radiology service, or by contributing their expertise in a multi-disciplinary team meeting to which another clinician has brought the patient's records, but not the patient – the total being about 200,000 decisions a day per million with possible resource consequences.

These clinical services are of direct value to patients, provided, of course, that:

- they are doing the **right** things to
- the **right** patients and
- doing them **right** and, each year
- doing them **better, safer, greener,** and **cheaper.**

There are, however, support services which are not clinical: management, education, research and Information Technology (IT). Decisions have to be made about how much money should be allocated for these purposes.

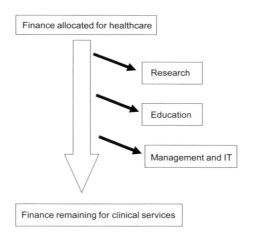

Figure Question 2.1 'Top Slicing' money before the funding of clinical care

What is the value of management?

Someone has to pay clinicians, buy the equipment they use and carry out a myriad of activities, such as organising the car parking; someone defined a modern hospital as a set of departments united only by complaints about car parking! Resources have to be invested in management or administration – the term varies from one service to another – but how much of the resources? The answer is as little as is necessary for the effective administration of the service, but there is no evidence-based formula that can be used to answer this question.

There are no randomised trials of health services with 5% management costs compared to health services with 10% management costs, in part because of the difficulty in defining what is meant by a 'management cost'. It has been argued that healthcare management illustrates Parkinson's Law perfectly – management tasks increase in direct proportion to the amount of management time available to tackle them. (1) The logical conclusion of this principle, a hospital fully staffed with administrators but without a single patient, was compellingly portrayed in the BBC television series *Yes, Minister!* The costs of management increase as the amount of regulation increases, however. If, for example, it is mandated that clinicians must have an externally validated appraisal of their competence each year, a system has to be set up to manage this process and management costs increase as a consequence, so managers can cannot be blamed for all the increase in the costs of management.

Whatever the proportion of resources spent on management, no-one argues with the fact that some investment is necessary. If all management costs were cut, the service would grind to a halt very quickly. Just how quickly depends on how much stock is available, but in a hospital working on 'lean' principles, with very little stock in the pharmacy, the laboratory, or the linen store, the service would grind to a halt within a week. The same cannot be said for investment in education or research. If such investment were cut, the impact would take longer to manifest.

The analysis of the value of management is very difficult, as is the evaluation of the marginal benefit of increasing the investment in management or the marginal cost of cutting management. A simpler approach, with no evidence that it is any less effective, is just to assume that bureaucracy inevitably grows in size and simply impose a cut, decided arbitrarily. The White Paper, *Equity and Excellence: Liberating the NHS*, included the simple clear commitment to 'reduce management costs by over 45% in the next four years'. Obviously games will be played about what actually is a management cost but a commitment of this size and clarity is bound to have a big effect.

Furthermore, the White Paper makes clear that the aim of this is not only to reduce overhead costs but to free up the time of frontline staff to look after patients, and to innovate by reducing the number of reports they have to make to management.

What is the value of education?

The clinical staff of a health service is the resource that delivers the service to patients. They need buildings and equipment and management support, but the clinical staff is of central importance in realising the potential benefit that investment in equipment and buildings offers. Where do staff come from?

Health service staff are recruited as a result of investing in an advertisement, but to ensure that there are sufficient trained staff to recruit, a health service has to address that standard business question: 'make or buy?'

The attraction of buying staff is obvious. The service only has to pay the salaries of the staff it employs, and not meet the costs of training. A service can invest a significant sum in the training of replacements, or it can buy the clinical staff produced by another country. Germany, for example, had a policy of allowing everyone who was qualified to do so to go to university. The predictable result was that it produced an 'Ärzteschwämme' – a flood of doctors. As resources became scarcer, medical unemployment and under-employment emerged, and the English NHS was able to meet its need by buying the 'products' of German higher education and health services. This is a simple market issue. There is, however, a moral issue when developed countries buy the professional staff trained by poor countries. Moreover, even this view, driven by the late Robin Cook's 'ethical foreign policy', is now under review because the remittances sent home by professionals working in rich countries are now of major economic importance to some poor countries.

The White Paper, *Equity and Excellence: Liberating the NHS*, emphasises that the NHS spends billions of pounds on education but wants to change their spend from a top-sliced budget 'to give employers greater autonomy and accountability for planning and developing the workforce'.

Within education lurks a resource whose value is often underused – the library service. Knowledge is the enemy of disease. The application of what we know will have a bigger impact on health and disease than any drug or technology likely to be introduced in the next decade. By managing knowledge better, eight major problems of healthcare can be minimised:

- errors;
- poor quality care delivery;
- poor experience of patients;
- waste;
- unknowing variations in policy and practice;
- failure to introduce high value interventions;
- uncritical adoption of low value interventions;
- failure to recognise uncertainty and ignorance.

Most organisations could increase value significantly by recognising that the most valuable resource in their library is the librarian and ensuring that librarians are as active in the clinic and the boardroom as in education.

What is the value of research?

The value of investment in research is more complicated. Again, a health service could answer the make or buy question by 'buying' research outputs from other countries, or subscribing to journals or the Cochrane Library, or simply by using the free service of Pub Med from the National Library of Medicine in the US, and the increasingly influential free knowledge sources such as the Public Library of Science, BioMed Central, Pub Med Central and Google.

The economic benefits

There are, however, a number of reasons why health services would be ill-advised not to invest in the support of research.

- The proportion of the most frequently cited articles funded by industry increased over time and was equal to the proportion funded by government or public sources. Academics may be losing control of the research agenda. (2)
- Conclusions in trials funded by for profit organisations may be more positive due to biased interpretation of trial results.(3) Constraints on the publication rights were described in 40 (91%) of the protocols from 1994/5 and 22 (50%) noted that the [industry] sponsor either owned the data or needed to approve the manuscript or both.(4)

If the health service does not invest in research, the evidence base will be increasingly stocked with industry-funded research, and if decisions are to be evidence-based there will be increased investment in drugs simply because the evidence base for, to give two examples, walking therapy for arterial disease or psychological therapy for depression, will be much weaker without health service investment.

There is, however, another factor which has to be taken into consideration when deciding how much to invest in research, namely, the value that such investment has for the economy of the country as a whole.

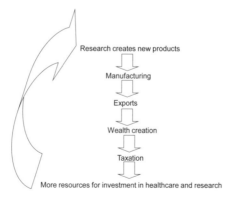

Figure Question 2.2 The benefits of research to the economy

If an improvement in the health of the population is regarded as an economic good, as it should be, the return for society from investment in research can be shown to be valuable. A major review of the economic benefits of investing in the US National Institutes of Health (NIH) concluded that *'the public return on investment has been substantial. Although results have led to increases in healthcare expenditures, health gains were large and valuable.'* (5)

If investment in research can be justified, the next question is to ask: how much? The National Health Service Research and Development programme was set up on the recommendation of a House of Lords Committee, with the aim of investing 1.5% of NHS resources in the direct cost of research and the 'support of research'. This support is needed to meet the extra costs in a clinical service in which clinicians are carrying out research. This policy was a necessary consequence of the introduction of a healthcare market because the total costs of care in a hospital with a large research programme were often greater than the costs of care in a hospital with no research.

The debate about the value of research was stimulated in 2006 in the United Kingdom by the decision to review the need for two publicly funded research programmes, one focusing on 'laboratory research', the other focusing on 'practice-orientated research'. 'Practice-orientated research' is a term chosen rather than 'clinical research' which has come to mean laboratory research on the basic mechanisms of disease, as opposed to research on how best to prevent or treat disease today (6,7). Practice-orientated research can bring rapid benefit to those who manage or pay for healthcare. For example, there has long been uncertainty about the relative merits of venous and arterial catheters in the management of patients with severe trauma. A well designed and executed research project produced an unequivocal answer of immediate use to the healthcare providers and payers:

> *Pulmonary Artery Catheter (PAC) guided therapy did not improve survival or organ function but was associated with more complications than central venous catheter (CVC) guided therapy. These results, when considered with those of previous studies, suggest that the PAC should not be used routinely for the management of acute lung injury.* (8)

The value of research to patients

Research results are often of value to patients, but the immediate value of being involved in research is less clear. It is true that it can give the patient the opportunity of a new treatment not routinely available but the new treatments being tested may be ineffective. It is also true that patients in research are looked after very carefully according to strict protocols. The involvement of children in leukaemia research, for instance, has helped transform that disease from a certain killer to one that is often cured.

For many patients, however, the value of involvement in research is the sense of altruism. The Million Women Collaborative Study in England recruited a million women as they attended for breast cancer screening who now feel that they are not research subjects, but partners in the war against breast cancer.

The White Paper, *Equity and Excellence: Liberating the NHS,* was very clear in emphasising that 'research is even more important [to the NHS] when budgets are under pressure'.

How much should be invested in information technology (IT) to maximise value?

A modern health service cannot run without computers. Some investment is therefore necessary, but how much to maximise value? There is no simple answer.

The cost of the investment is usually easy to estimate, although the history of IT investment in both industry and the public sector is that, unless the contracts are very carefully drafted, the actual cost is often greater than the planned cost. Administrative benefits are easier to describe, but more difficult to measure in financial terms. IT can reduce the staffing costs of healthcare administration but the magnitude of these management savings has never been clearly estimated because:

- computerisation has crept into hospitals piecemeal while, at the same time,
- administration has become more complex.

There is, however, another benefit from IT investment: a clinical benefit for patients (9,10). There is good enough evidence that investment in IT can:

- reduce clinical errors
- increase the effectiveness of healthcare by faster uptake of high value interventions
- reduce the harmful effects of healthcare by preventing unknowing prescription of drugs that interact with one another

More evidence is needed, particularly about the contribution of clinical decision support systems – software that reminds and alerts both clinicians and patients about clinical actions that should or should not be considered, but the evidence that some investment will produce clinical benefit is 'good enough' (11).

The decision to spend some resources on IT for clinical benefit is not difficult. The difficulty lies in deciding how much, bearing in mind the fact that investment in IT almost certainly is governed (as is so much healthcare investment) by the law of diminishing returns with, at best, a flattening of the curve relating benefit to investment and, probably, a point of optimality beyond which the net benefit declines. IT, like all technology, can do harm as well as good. The decision is more complicated than the decision about investment in IT to increase the productivity of administration. The benefits of investment in clinical IT are not 'cash releasing', that is, they do not allow the number of clinical staff to be reduced. The main justification for investment in clinical IT is that it obviates some of the need for additional senior clinical staff by ensuring that less experienced clinical staff have their decisions guided by clinical pathways, prompts and reminders.

The transformation of healthcare by IT

Putting a computer system unthinkingly into an unstructured mess of consultations and clinical encounters will not, by itself, transform the mess and may increase the confusion. One study showed that mortality increased following the introduction of computerised prescribing. (12)

On the other hand the introduction of technology as part of a process of transformation can be revolutionary. Policy-makers and managers think they run the world but, as the historian Lynn White Jr. demonstrated, with evidence, history has been written by people who spend their lives 'scribbling', namely priests and politicians. They have overlooked the dramatic changes that technology introduced, in part because those who developed technology in times past could not write. For example, the introduction of the heavy plough led inexorably to the development of the manorial system in England because it forced villagers to combine their oxen. (13) Revolution is quietly taking place in healthcare, driven by technology, but many decision-makers do not realise what is happening or seek to harness the revolutionary forces of knowledge, patients and information technology to transform care.

The benefits of IT are not simply a reduction in administrative costs; they result from its revolutionary, disruptive impact. The adjective 'disruptive' became famous as a result of Clayton Christensen's book *The Innovator's Dilemma*, subtitled *When New Technologies Cause Great Firms to Fail* (14). In This book he describes how innovations can be disruptive and paradigm-changing, and those companies that are complacent or do not appreciate this become extinct. Christensen then turned his attention to healthcare and, with two medical co-authors, published *The Innovator's Prescription,* subtitled *Disruptive Solutions for Healthcare* (15). The disruptive technology is the Internet, and all that flows from it, including patient power.

The appropriate use of technology will transform healthcare. The focus on 'big' IT projects distracts attention from a multitude of changes taking place that are initiated and enabled by technology. Sometimes the technology has direct financial cost, other initiatives use the Web, emails or open source software, but the latter often have service implications and costs. The result of those forces is sometimes called e-Health – a term best defined by giving examples.

- The development of 'Connected Health' networks.
- Email consultations by patients.
- The support of disabled people in their own homes with tele-care.

- Describing care pathways explicitly using the 'Map of Medicine' software.
- The delivery of community care by professionals using robust 'tablets' to record and communicate key information about patients.
- Sending laboratory results directly to patients.

Companies such as Cisco and Intel, big telephone companies such as BT and Telstra, and web companies like Google and Microsoft will have as big an impact on healthcare in the 21st century as had the pharmaceutical giants in the 20th century.

It is of interest to note that in the twelve paragraphs devoted to the 'Information Revolution', the White Paper did not refer to information technology but to the production and use of information, particularly from and by patients. There has always been a view that we focus too much on information technology, sometimes called information systems, whereas if we were to focus on clinical systems then we would find that the Internet plus Microsoft Word plus the iPod plus some proprietary patient record system would be able to support those clinical systems.

Questions for reflection when teaching or developing networks

If using these in network building or teaching, give one of the questions to the group and ask them to work in pairs to reflect on the question for three minutes; try to get people who do not know one another to work together.

When taking feedback, let each pair make only one point. In the interests of equity, if you start with the pair on the left-hand side of the room for the first question, start with the pair on the right-hand side of the room for the second question.

- What types of research would not be funded if all research funding were left to industry?
- What would be the advantages and disadvantages of cutting training budgets by £2 billion annually and recruiting all professional clinical staff from the European Union?
- What steps could be taken to reduce the possibility that investment in information technology would not result in a high value infrastructure?

References

(1)   Parkinson, C.N.C. (1958) *Parkinson's Law, or The Pursuit of Progress.* Penguin.

(2)   Patsopoulos, N. et al (2006) Origin and Funding of the Most Frequently Cited Papers in Medicine. *BMJ* 332: *1061-64.*

(3)   Als-Nielsen, B. et al (2003) Association of Sources of Funding and Conclusions in Randomised Controlled Trials. *JAMA* 290: *921-928.*

(4)   Gøtzsche, P. et al (2006) Constraints on Publication Rights in Industry-initiated Controlled Trials. *JAMA 295*: *1645-1646.*

(5)   Johnston, S.C. et al (2006)   Effect of a US National Institutes of Health Programme of Clinical Trials on Public Health. *Lancet 367: 1319-1327.*

(6)   Horton, R (2006) Health Research in the UK; the price of success. *Lancet 368: 93-9.*

(7)   Rothwell, P.M (2006) Funding for Practice-orientated Research.   *Lancet 368: 262-266.*

(8)   The NHLBI ARDS Clinical Trials Network: PAC versus CVC to Guide the Treatment of Acute Lung Injury (2006) *NEJM 354*: 2213–2224.

(9)   Greenes, R.A. (2006) *Clinical Decision Support; the Road Ahead.* Academic Press.

(10)   Osheroff, J.A. et al (2005) *Improving Health Outcomes with Clinical Decision Support.* HIMSS.

(11)   Halamka, J.D. (2006) Health Information Technology: Shall we wait for the Evidence? *Ann. Int. Med. 144:775-776.*

(12)   Han, Y.Y. et al (2005) Unexpected Increased Mortality after Computerized Physician Order Entry System. *Paediatrics 116: 1506-1512.*

(13)   White Jr., L. (1966) *Medieval Technology and Social Change.* Oxford University Press.

(14)   Christensen, C.M. (1997) *The Innovator's Dilemma.* Harvard University Press.

(15)   Christensen, C.M, Grossman, J.H. and Hwang, J. (2009) *The Innovator's Prescription.* McGraw-Hill.

Question 3: Have we distributed the money for clinical care to different parts of the country by a method that recognises both variation in need and maximises value for the whole population?

This section will:

- explain the methods that can be used to allocate resources to different populations;
- highlight the difficulty in doing this to the satisfaction of all parts of the community.

By the end of this section you will have an understanding of:

- the limits of epidemiology and the need for judgement in decision-making;
- the tensions inherent in any system for allocating finite resources to populations with different levels of need;
- the system used by the NHS for resource allocation.

Publicly funded healthcare is designed to meet need, and resources are allocated on the basis of need, but the definition of need is not always straightforward. The quantification of the need of different populations is a complicated issue, which often requires a very simple solution.

In a developed country, the single most important factor is the age of the population served, because most diseases become more common in older age groups. However, there are other factors that determine the health needs of a population, notably poverty. Almost all diseases are more common among poor people. The definition of 'poor' itself is not universally agreed. It can be defined in absolute terms, for example with respect to a certain level of income, or in relative terms, for example with respect to the distribution of income in the population. Furthermore, there is discussion as to whether poverty itself is the only factor or whether deprivation, a sense of alienation and low worth, is a separate variable and needs recognition. In calculating risk for heart disease, for example, the Scottish Executive has identified all the people living in particularly deprived communities as being of high priority, even though all the individuals in those communities may not be very poor.

If the desire is to maximise value by matching resources to need, then resources must be allocated taking into account not only the age distribution of the population but also the level of poverty and deprivation within the community. In the United Kingdom, the simplest approach has been to use the Standardised Mortality Ratio. Obviously, poverty and deprivation cause disability as well as early mortality, but the Standardised Mortality Ratio reflects levels of disability and morbidity within the population and is used as an indicator of health need, either alone or with additional weighting to take into account the poverty of the population.

This is not an exact science. Those representing populations favoured by the formula often feel that the formula does not reflect them sufficiently; those representing populations that are losers on account of the formula may feel, on the other hand and not surprisingly, that the formula employed makes too much allowance for deprivation.

Questions for reflection when teaching or developing networks

If using these in network building or teaching, give one of the questions to the group and ask them to work in pairs to reflect on the question for three minutes; try to get people who do not know one another to work together.

When taking feedback, let each pair make only one point. In the interests of equity, if you start with the pair on the left-hand side of the room for the first question, start with the pair on the right-hand side of the room for the second question.

- Is it better to think of 'the best' way of allocating resources, or 'the least worst' way?
- What measures could be used to assess the degree to which a policy of allocating resources in proportion to need, had been successful?
- What is the case for allocating resources not only on differences in the incidence of disease and mortality in different populations, but also taking into account the levels of poverty in the populations?

Question 4: Has money been distributed to different patient groups by decision-making that is not only equitable but also maximises value for the whole population?

This section will:

- explain programme budgeting;
- give an account of the process of marginal analysis and the assessment of allocative efficiency;
- review the issues relating to equity and fairness.

By the end of this chapter you will have an understanding of:

- the strengths and limitations of programme budgeting;
- the difference between technical and allocative efficiency;
- the concept of equity.

If we were to arrive in some new, uninhabited world with no investment at all in healthcare, and were asked to design a health service, life would be relatively, though not completely, straightforward. Hellish decisions would still have to be made about how much money should be allocated to patients with cancer and how much to people with mental illness.

A few people have had the opportunity to do this when they have been appointed to manage health services in small but very rich states, where a massive increase in investment is planned, but even they often inherit the consequences of years, sometimes decades, of chaotic investment. In most developed countries, the person who comes new to a job managing or paying for healthcare knows that they are going to inherit a mess. Even the best managed services are messes, using the term 'mess' to mean a management problem for which there is

- no ideal solution, and for which
- every solution will create further problems.

Budget sheets usually present expenditure as it relates to institutions such as hospitals and community services, or to broad divisions within a hospital that bear little relevance to a specific health problem such as breast cancer, or type of problem such as respiratory disease – for example, by presenting information describing expenditure on medicine, surgery, laboratory services, and imaging. A person with cancer of the bowel, or almost any other serious problem, will use resources from all four. To answer Question 4 with any validity, it is necessary to organise the budgets on the basis of the health problems that the clinicians are tackling.

The need for programme budgeting

Increasingly, the need for organising budgets which focus on programmes of care has been recognised, and the Department of Health in England has defined a set of Programme Budget Categories, based on the International Classification of Disease, to accelerate this trend. The 23 categories are:

1. Infectious Diseases
2. Cancers and Tumours, including those with suspected, or at risk of developing, cancer
3. Blood Disorders
4. Endocrine, Nutritional and Metabolic Problems
5. Mental Health Problems
6. Problems of Learning Disability
7. Neurological System Problems
8. Vision Problems
9. Hearing Problems
10. Circulation Problems
11. Respiratory Problems, including Tuberculosis and Sleep Apnoea
12. Dental Problems, including Preventive Checks and Community Surveys
13. Gastrointestinal Problems
14. Skin Problems
15. Musculoskeletal Problems
16. Trauma and Injuries, including Burns
17. Genitourinary Problems

18. Maternity & Reproductive health
19. Neonates
20. Poisoning
21. Healthy Individuals
22. Social Care Needs – problems related to life-management difficulty, and problems related to care-provider dependency
23. Other

Budgets for individual conditions

Budgets can be set at a finer level of granularity, at the level of the specific health problem – for breast cancer, rheumatoid arthritis, or cystic fibrosis, for example. Indeed, Porter & Teisberg, in their analysis (1) of the reasons why competition has failed to deliver high quality healthcare in the United States, argue that it is essential to do this and to encourage competition between 'Integrated Patient Units', delivering care to patients with specific conditions, because competition between hospitals or insurance companies is too broad to have any meaning.

A programme budget for public health

Since 1974 when public health services in the United Kingdom were moved from Local Government to the NHS, there has been continuing debate about spending on health promotion and disease prevention. Should spending on cervical cancer screening, for example, be considered part of a cancer programme budget or a prevention programme budget, or indeed a women's health programme budget? This debate has been clarified by the decision, announced in the White Paper, *Equity and Excellence: Liberating the NHS*, published in July 2010, that 'we will ring-fence the public health budget' which will include immunisation and screening. This will, of course, bring up a new question: how much of the total should go into the prevention budget?

Maximising allocative efficiency

Allocative efficiency is maximised when resources are allocated or distributed among various programme budgets in such a way that it is not possible to increase harm, increase benefit, or decrease harm by moving a single pound from one budget to another. This is sometimes called the 'point of indifference' (3). From the point of view of the NHS, allocative efficiency should be described as the value derived from the allocation of resources among the various programme budgets. Having allocated resources to a programme budget heading, for example respiratory disease or, to be more 'granular', asthma, those who manage healthcare have to ensure that they deliver services that are effective at low cost. This is sometimes called technical efficiency, to distinguish it from allocative efficiency. Value is maximised when both allocative and technical efficiency are maximised.

Programme budgeting for better value decision-making

While the terms 'budgeting' and 'budgets' are normally applied to current and/or future allocations of expenditure, in the context of programme budgeting and programme budgets, it is assumed that they can be applied to past allocations as well. The principle underlying programme budgeting is very simple. If decisions are to be made about broadly defined healthcare objectives and priorities – for example, what are the objectives associated with care of the elderly? What relative priorities are attached to the treatment of cancer compared with the prevention of heart disease? – then data should be provided in similarly broad terms to match the nature of the choices. (8)

Tools are being developed to appraise options in more detail than simple cost-effectiveness, expressed as a 'cost per QALY' or 'cost per DALY'. One approach has been the development of two criteria:

- the Disease Impact Number is the number of people with a disease of whom one will benefit if an intervention were to be offered to all patients;
- the Population Impact Number is the number of people in a particular population who would benefit if the intervention were to be introduced to that population. (2)

When extra resources are available for allocation, or cuts have to be made, or consideration is being given to increasing one programme's budget by reducing the budget of another programme, a technique called marginal analysis is used. (4) This assumes that all past decision-making which led to the programme budgets having their current form was explicit, evidence based, and logical. There is no record of this having happened in healthcare either. The best brains in economics have wrestled with the problems of:

- eliciting preferences;
- making choices equitably;
- maximising value.

There is unfortunately, but not surprisingly, no simple formula to resolve the terrible dilemma that decision-takers have to face (5, 6) because in the end these are issues decided by public values (7) not arithmetic.

Between-programme marginal analysis

The questions that need to be tackled by people who pay for or manage healthcare resources, having decided first how to allocate resources to different geographical populations, are set out below.

- Has money been distributed to different patient groups, e.g. people with cancer and people with lung disease, in such a way as to maximise value?
- Are all the interventions being offered likely to confer a good balance of benefit and harm, at affordable cost, for this group of patients?
- Are the patients most likely to benefit and least likely to be harmed from the interventions clearly defined?
- Could each patient's experience be improved?
- Is effectiveness being maximised?
- Are the risks of care being minimised?
- Can costs be reduced without increasing harm or reducing benefit?

The first question in this list focuses on the allocation of resources and analysis of the effect of moving resources between two different groups of patients, for example, asking 'should we switch resources from mental health to respiratory disease or *vice versa*?'

The task of measuring costs and benefits should be done through marginal analysis. This involves starting with a particular mix of services and analysing changes in that mix. If resources can be shifted to produce greater benefit then this should be done. (9)

This type of approach has to be taken and the common currency used is not only financial but also QALYS (Quality Adjusted Life Years) or DALYS (Disability Adjusted Life Years). This, however, is difficult to manage at local level. The aim is to reach what economists call the point of optimality, or maximum allocative efficiency.

When the consumption and production markets are in equilibrium, and when consumers' rates of indifference are equal to the economy's ability to transform one good into the others, we are in a position called Pareto optimality, named after the economist Vilfredo Pareto. In an economy that is in a Pareto-optimal state, it is impossible to make someone better off (that is, increase a person's welfare) without making someone else worse off. Under such a situation, the economy has reached a state of allocative efficiency, although, as we shall see in the next section, this rests on a number of assumptions. (10)

The simple approach is to see how the relationship between spend and outcome for one population compares with spend and outcome for another population, and the information allowing this comparison is now provided by the Department of Health, the Information Centre for Health and Social Care, and the Public Health Observatories. Put very simply, spend is related to outcome, if outcome data are available, and each Primary Care Trust can compare their spend and outcome not only with that of all other Primary Care Trusts but also with Primary Care Trusts looking after similar populations.

Within programme marginal analysis

One of the benefits of using programme budgeting is that it does relate to medical specialties so that it is possible to compare, within any population, the amount of resources committed to, for example, asthma compared with the amount invested in chronic obstructive pulmonary disease (COPD) or the management of sleep apnoea, as shown in Figure Q4.1.

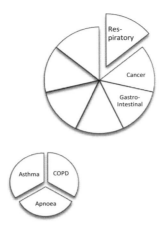

Figure Q4.1 Intra-programme marginal analysis

If a decision is made to hold the programme budget constant then local clinicians and patient groups can be engaged in a debate about the pressures on different services and the priorities that should be given to switching resources from one to another.

Within system marginal analysis

It is, of course, possible and essential to repeat this type of analysis within any single system. Within the amount of money committed to COPD, for example, it is possible to consider the benefits and harms of switching resources between smoking cessation to prevent COPD, telephone support for people with COPD, triple therapy, and pulmonary rehabilitation (Figure Q4.2).

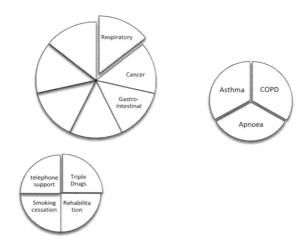

Figure Q4.2 Intra-system marginal analysis

Within systems, marginal analysis should also challenge the use of resources within each system to maximise value. Thus to maintain the same value, it is essential, before deciding to switch resources from one type of therapy to another, or between COPD and asthma, to ask the same question of each of the systems within the respiratory disease programme budget: 'Can more value be derived from the resources within the system?'

The end of the era of marginal analysis

Although the focus has been on marginal analysis the focus in the future will not be on the margins but on the whole budget.

In years of plenty a clinician would bid for £400k for developing a sleep apnoea service and if they got the money it would be added to their budget, having been denied to some other bidder.

In years of famine, the bidder will be reminded that they are already spending £3M on the sleep apnoea service, and even more important that there is already £56M being spent on respiratory disease services for their population. So what they should do is to find from the sleep apnoea budget, or if that is difficult for a new service with a small budget, look across the whole £56M budget for the opportunities for disinvestment from interventions of lower value.

In addition, all health services will move into an era of population-based planning; what needs can be foreseen from demographic changes and technological developments, and within fixed budgets what should be deemed high value and what can be identified as being of lower value needing to be reduced, or stopped as part of a plan to maximize value.

The Limitations of Programme Budgeting

Language constructs reality rather than reflecting it (11)

Equity: the quality of being equal or fair; impartiality; even-handed dealing (12)

In order to classify expenditure by programme, the patient has to have a diagnosis and this means that the focus of the decision-maker's eye is always on treatment services, but there is a great deal of expenditure on patients before the diagnosis is made, for example on the investigation of a person who has a headache.

Furthermore, preventative services which relate to more than one disease, smoking cessation for example, may be overlooked. It is difficult to prepare a programme budget for prevention, as the Health England Committee found, and their task commenced with the need to define both preventative services and the spending on them:

A single definition of preventative health care spending should be adopted. A recommended definition is: the total public and private spend on primary and secondary prevention, health promotion, family planning, early years, school and youth health services, national screening programmes, public health programmes for communicable and non-communicable disease, epidemiological surveillance and public health administration. (13)

Maximising value, equitably

It is important to distinguish between two similar-sounding, but quite different, concepts: 'equality' and 'equity'. The former implies equal shares of something; the latter, a 'fair' or 'just' distribution, which may or may not result in equal shares. (14)

Justice ... requires meeting health care needs fairly under resource constraints, and this, in turn, requires limiting care in a publicly accountable way. (15)

Programme budgeting based on the International Classification of Disease (ICD) creates what sociologists would call a medical construction of healthcare, which is only one perspective, a health service viewed through a medical lens. Imagine now that the high level classification was not based on the ICD but on gender, age, ethnic group or socio-economic group. A completely different budget structure would be developed, and different decisions would have to be faced. Instead of asking the question, 'has money been distributed to different patients groups, such as people with cancer or with mental health problems', decision-makers would be asking questions such as:

- Has money been distributed equitably to different age groups, e.g. children or adults or elderly people?
- Has money been distributed equitably to meet the different needs of men and women?
- Has money been distributed equitably to different ethnic groups, e.g. people from south Asia or from Africa?
- Has money been distributed equitably to different socio-economic groups?
- Are we overlooking the needs of people with rare diseases?

There is evidence that if these questions are asked, using these lenses, many health services appear to spend less resources, relative to the needs of the group, on minority ethnic groups, women, older people, poor people, and less well-educated people.

It could be argued that this is the result of issues unrelated to values, for example the literacy of poorly educated people. This, however, ducks the issue. The decision-maker needs to form a judgement about whether healthcare resources should be invested in services specifically for these groups, such as in services for sickle cell disease, or in ancillary services, such as the provision of interpreters, which could increase utilisation. These decisions create what has been called 'public value' (16).

The allocation of money to children's services poses a particular challenge. The amount of resources allocated to children is difficult to discern because children are treated by every service except geriatrics, yet the only ICD budget heading is 'neonates'. The amount invested in improving the health of children needs to take into account not only the present needs of children but also the values we place on children and their future contribution to society. At a meeting in Oxford's Town Hall, convened to deplore that lack of investment in services for elderly people, the mood of indignation mounted as speaker after speaker called for more resources for the elderly. Then one woman, herself indubitably elderly, stood up and said: 'Let's face it, important though we are, it is children who need the resources.' This was greeted with universal applause, including from those who had called, not a few minutes before, for more resources for older patients.

Because there is no exact formula (17) to determine the allocation of resources that would result in perfect equity, the process by which the allocation decisions are made becomes of great importance for example to make sure that the decision makers stick to the agreed principles. The test that is gaining popularity is whether or not they can give an account of the reasonableness with which they carried out their task.

Accountability for reasonableness is the idea that the reasons or rationales for important limit-setting decisions should be publicly available. In addition, these reasons must be ones that 'fair-minded' people can agree are relevant to pursuing appropriate patient care under necessary resource constraints. This is our central thesis, and it needs some explanation.

By 'fair-minded', we do not simply mean our friends or people who just happen to agree with us. We mean people who in principle seek to cooperate with others on terms they can justify to each other. Indeed, fair-minded people accept rules of the game – or sometimes seek rule changes – that promote the game's essential skills and the excitement their use produces. (15)

These are fine words but vague, and vary from one country to another; there is an assertion, for example, that the words 'fair' and 'reasonable' have no equivalents in other European languages (let alone non European ones) (18). Fortunately these authors also describe four conditions that can be used to assess the reasonableness of the allocation decision-making process:

1. openness to the public;
2. objectivity and logic of the principles and criteria used to compare competing bids;
3. the existence of an appeal process;
4. some form of regulation to make sure that conditions 1-3 are met.

Real world problems

For most decision-makers, programme budgeting and marginal analyses are at present impossible. They are pressed to pay for some new drug or procedure and the cost-effectiveness information they are given, cost per QALY if they are fortunate, does not help them decide whether or not the investment of funds in this drug will increase or decrease the health of that group of patients, taking into account the fact that the decision to invest will result in the same amount of money being diverted from another use.

Those making the decisions are not able to do so as an academic exercise. They have to make and take decisions:

- with limited time and deadlines;
- without all the knowledge they need;
- without a computer program that can do it all for them.

They have to use 'bounded rationality'(19) and good judgement. The judgements are, in the words of NICE, the National Institute of Health and Clinical Excellence, 'social value judgements' and their principles, drawn up with very wide involvement, are publicly expressed in a document with that title. (20) This document covers a wide range of issues, including very difficult problems of distributive justice and the tension between maximising value for society as a whole, while responding to the needs of an individual in desperate circumstances, what is called the 'rule of rescue'.

In the White Paper, *Equity and Excellence: Liberating the NHS,* the government emphasised that one of its most important principles is 'fairness' but it is not possible to define fairness by a formula. The population served needs to accept that not all needs can be met and that all that can be done is to make decisions openly and fairly – itself a value judgement.

Questions for reflection when teaching or developing networks

If using these in network building or teaching, give one of the questions to the group and ask them to work in pairs to reflect on the question for three minutes; try to get people who do not know one another to work together.

When taking feedback, let each pair make only one point. In the interests of equity, if you start with the pair on the left-hand side of the room for the first question, start with the pair on the right-hand side of the room for the second question.

- What are the principal weaknesses in managing the allocation of resources based on programme budgets which reflect the disease groupings of the International Classification of Disease (ICD)?
- Should disease prevention have its own programme budget or be included in the relevant disease specific programme budget?
- What is the best way to describe the difference between equity and equality when under pressure on a local radio station?

References

(1)   Porter, M. and Teisberg, E. (2006) *Redefining Healthcare.* Harvard Business School Press.

(2)   Moore, M.H. (1997) *Creating Public Value.* Harvard University Press.

(3)   Heller, R.F. (2005) *Evidence for Population Health.* Oxford University Press.

(4)   Enthoven, A. (1971) *How Much is Enough?* Harper and Row.

(5)   Donaldson, C. and Mitton, C. (2004) *Priority Setting Toolkit.* Blackwell.

(6)   Sen, A.K. (1982) *Choice, Welfare and Measurement.* Blackwell.

(7)   Kahneman, D. and Tversky, A. (2000) *Choices, Values and Frames*. Cambridge University Press.

(8)   Mooney, G.H., Russell, E.M., and Weir, R.D. (1980) *Choices for Health Care*. The Macmillan Press.

(9)   Mitton, C. and Donaldson, C. (2004) *Priority setting toolkit. A guide to the use of economics in healthcare decision-making*. BMJ Publishing Group. (p.18)

(10)   Rice, T. (1998) *The Economics of Health Reconsidered*. Health Administration Press. (pp. 19-20).

(11)   Whorf, B.L. (1956) *Language, Thought and Reality. Selected Writings of Benjamin Lee Whorf*. MIT Press.

(12)   Stevenson, A. (ed.) (2007) *Shorter Oxford English Dictionary*. Oxford University Press.

(13)   Department of Health (2009) *Prevention and Preventative Health Spending*. Department of Health.

(14)   Arrow, K. (1951) *Social Choice and Individual Values*. Wiley.

(15)   Rice, T. (1998) *The Economics of Health Reconsidered*. Health Administration Press.

(16)   Daniels, N. and Sabin, J.E. (2008) *Setting Limits Fairly, Learning to Share Resources for Health*. Oxford University Press. (p.44)

(17)   Persad, G. et al (2009) Principles for Allocation of Scarce Resources; *Lancet* 373:423-431.

(18)   Wierzbicka, A. (2006) *English: Meaning and Culture*. Oxford University Press.

(19)   Simon, H. (1997) *Administrative Behavior*. Free Press.

(20)   NICE (2008) *Social Value Judgements* available at http://www.nice.org.uk/media/C18/30/SVJ2PUBLICATION 2008.pdf

Question 5: Are all the interventions offered likely to confer a good balance of benefit and harm, at an affordable cost, for this group of patients?

This section will:

- explain the difference between absolute and relative benefits, and the impact the method of presentation has on decision-makers;
- discuss the limited usefulness of the term 'effective';
- review how the Quality Adjusted Life Year (QALY) is used in assessing costs and benefits;
- consider the grounds on which a decision not to allocate resources can be challenged.

By the end of this section you will have an understanding of:

- what is meant by framing and how the bias that framing causes can be prevented;
- the difference between the QALY and the ICER (the Incremental Cost Effectiveness Ratio);
- the need to have different methods for appraising diagnostic tests and treatments;
- how to talk about new tests and treatments without using the term 'effective'.

For any group of patients there are many possible interventions that could be offered. These can be classified using the simple matrix below.

	High value	Low value
Provided	A	B
Not provided	C	D

Figure Question 5.1 The imperfect relationship between provision and benefit

It may be that the service under consideration is providing only the interventions in Box A, and cannot identify any in Boxes B or C – the perfect service. This is not common. Usually it is possible to identify interventions of type B, C and D. The payer and provider must have a strategy for each of the four situations:

> for A – keep them going, and do them better each year;
> for B – start them stopping;
> for C – start them starting;
> for D – stop them starting.

The person paying for or managing healthcare has to begin a process of:

- increasing the proportion of interventions that are high value;
- decreasing the number of interventions that are of lower value.

When the process of value improvement starts, the debate usually focuses on interventions which:

- clinicians and patients want introduced;
- clinicians and patients want more of;
- payers want less of, or want to stop.

This leads to the need to have a method for appraising the value of a single intervention and the questions used to appraise new treatments, tests, or services have evolved in the last thirty years.

Appraising diagnostic tests

Doing the right thing does not only mean choosing the right treatment. It also means getting the diagnosis right before starting treatment. In part because of the greater availability of money for pharmaceutical rather than diagnostic research, the evidence base for diagnosis is less strong. Appraising screening tests and programmes is relatively simple because there is a defined population and the programme has a single aim. (1)   When tests are used for diagnosis, however, the problem is much more difficult because some people use the test with one aim, whereas others use the same test for a different reason. Furthermore, it may be that less rigorous criteria have been applied to new laboratory or imaging diagnostic tests than to new drugs, and the value of further investment in high technology diagnosis needs to be questioned.

An alternative approach set out in the book *Patient Centred Diagnosis*, (2) is that investment in technological methods of diagnosis should be appraised not only with respect to cost-effectiveness criteria, but also in comparison with investing resources to give clinicians more time to listen to patients, and then examine them properly.

Is this treatment effective?

This was the question of the 1970s, when the concept of effectiveness had been accepted. In the 1980s, concern about the adverse effects of healthcare became much more prominent – not the adverse effects arising from medical errors, but adverse effects inherent in the intervention itself.

Thalidomide was, and still is, the most powerful example but there were other dramatically harmful interventions. Many people have minor arrhythmias after a myocardial infarction, and some die when these minor arrhythmias became major. When drugs were developed that controlled some of these arrhythmias they became very popular and were widely used. Unfortunately, the case for introducing these drugs was based on a plausible theory, and some experimental evidence, but the evidence of benefit was not strong, and the evidence of harm was very weak. This was not because there was no harm, but because researchers were focused on the benefits. The effects of the term 'effectiveness' were, at that time, always considered to be good effects, but by the late 1980s those drugs were killing as many as 70,000 people in the United States every year. The saga is described in the book *Deadly Medicine: Why Tens of Thousands of Heart Patients Died in America's Worst Drug Disaster* by Thomas J. Moore. (3)

As a consequence, the key question for the 1990s became:

What are the benefits and harms of this intervention?

Evidence about the harm of interventions is less plentiful than evidence of benefit because:

- harms are less common than benefits and therefore
- research projects designed to demonstrate the benefits of a new treatment are often not big enough to demonstrate any harm it may cause.

This has led to the conclusion that *'for a future that combines benefit and harms assessment, systematic reviews will need to incorporate and integrate the best information from both randomised trials and observational studies'*. (4) Furthermore, during the 1990s, it became clear that the magnitude of the benefits and the harms needed to be expressed in absolute terms. Instead of expressing the results of a trial of a new treatment in relative terms, saying, for example, that the new treatment doubled the cure rate with only a 10% harm rate, it was clearer both to clinicians and patients if the number of patients receiving a benefit, and the number of patients being harmed were clearly described in absolute terms, or numbers, and not in percentages.

	METHOD OF EXPRESSING EFFECTS	
	Relative terms	Absolute terms
Benefits	100% improvement in cure rate	1 in 2,000 patients will be cured instead of 1 in 4,000
Harms	50% reduction in the rate of serious adverse effects	5 patients in every 100 die of side effects instead of 10

Figure Question 5.2 Expressing benefits and harms in absolute and relative terms

There is evidence that if a patient (5), doctor (6), or payer (7) is given information in relative terms, they are keener to use the new treatment than if the same data are presented in absolute terms.   This phenomenon, called 'framing', is, of course, well recognised by those who wish to promote new tests and treatments.

Also in the 1990s cost became a massive issue for all services, so the key question became:

Does this treatment do more good than harm at reasonable cost?

This raises the question of judging the reasonableness of cost, and cost benefit analysis was introduced, using the cost per Quality Adjusted Life Year (QALY) as the criterion, and NICE (The National Institute of Clinical Excellence) in England explains the use of this measure in its excellent publication on Social Value Judgements. NICE uses the QALY and the EQ-SD as measures because they take into account not only the increased life expectancy from an intervention, but also the quality of the increased life. In addition to recognising that much of healthcare is concerned with improving people's quality of life, it also reflects the value judgement that mere survival is an insufficient measure of benefit; and that the expected quality of life years gained also needs to be considered. Balancing life years gained and quality, involves social value judgements, some of which may be very difficult to make. The QALY also provides a 'common currency' which allows different interventions to be compared for different conditions. This allows NICE to make its decisions consistently, transparently and fairly. Cost-utility analysis cannot, however, be the sole basis for NICE's decisions and the Institute expects its advisory bodies to use their judgement when considering the results of cost-effectiveness analyses. (8)

Is this treatment of higher value than some of the interventions currently being offered to this group of patients?

The key issue for the 21st century is whether or not the innovation is the best value development for the programme of care to which it will contribute. The issue is not only the cost per QALY but also the opportunity cost of the innovation. This has also been termed the opportunity value, the value that could be realised by using the same amount of resource to invest in some other part of the service for that group of patients (9). NICE addresses this issue through the

Incremental Cost Effectiveness Ratio (ICER): *'the ratio of the difference in the mean costs of an intervention compared with the next best alternative (which could be no action or treatment) to the differences in the mean health outcomes. ICERs are expressed as cost (in £,) per QALY gained'. (6)*

NICE plays particular attention to this issue in its publications. To patient and professional groups the debate has often focused on whether a particular drug or intervention is above or below 'the NICE threshold'. However, NICE has always emphasised that there is no rigid threshold and that *'NICE has never identified an Incremental Cost Effectiveness Ratio (ICER) above which interventions should not be recommended and below which they should'.*

NICE has been much criticised, but every society that wishes to use limited resources for a whole population will need to develop a body like NICE (10).

One of the reasons for this book is the recognition that many societies now have more requests for funding cost-effective interventions that passed the test of reasonableness. The manager may bid to the payer for funding in the expectation that the budget will be increased if the case is good, but an increase in budget for one group of patients will, except in times of steady growth, lead the payer, or the manager of a large service faced with a bid from one department, to ask: Should we move money from another programme budget to meet the costs of this innovation?   The first response of the payer in future should, however, be the question: Is this new treatment or test of greater value than some other intervention being offered to this group of patients?

Clinicians are already quite good at ditching low value interventions in order to accommodate higher value interventions, but the process needs to become faster and more focused to get better value healthcare.

Challenging decisions

Increasingly the decisions made by those who are responsible for the allocation of resources are being challenged either by groups of patients or by individuals, and these challenges may be in the courts.

Whereas the public, the whole population, can accept that difficult decisions have to be made which do not allow every patient group to get all that it wants, the pressure group that represents a people with one condition are less tolerant. It campaigns for more resources for the people who form their constituency, using both the press and the courts to do so. The Alzheimer's Society, for example, challenged the decision of NICE not to recommend a drug for use in the NHS, a challenge that was eventually dismissed in the High Court and, as a commentary on the case pointed out, lost not only their case but some of their credibility because they had not revealed that the Society had received funding from the drug company that stood to benefit most if they had won. (11)

The individual patient can also challenge the decisions of public bodies and in England the NHS Confederation has published guidance for Primary Care Trusts to help them set priorities (12) and deal with individual requests (13) in this litigious environment.

Judgement is all

NICE bases its work on four social values:

- respect for autonomy;
- non-maleficence;
- beneficence;
- distributive justice.

These values are subjective and although evidence can illuminate debate the final decisions require good judgement.

Questions for reflection when teaching or developing networks

If using these in network building or teaching, give one of the questions to the group and ask them to work in pairs to reflect on the question for three minutes; try to get people who do not know one another to work together.

When taking feedback, let each pair make only one point. In the interests of equity, if you start with the pair on the left-hand side of the room for the first question, start with the pair on the right-hand side of the room for the second question.

- If an innovation has been shown to produce more benefit than harm at reasonable cost, is it not also reasonable to say that the funding required should come from the budget that already exists for that disease?

- On what grounds could a patient group challenge a decision by a health service not to provide a treatment?

- Preventive services are often claimed to reduce cost but does this mean they are cash-releasing?

References

(1)   Raffle, A. E. and Gray, J.A.M. (2007) *Screening: Evidence and Practice*. Oxford University Press.

(2)   Summerton, N. (2006) *Patient Centred Diagnosis*. Radcliffe Press.

(3)   Moore, T.J. (1995) *Deadly Medicine: Why Tens of Thousands of Heart Patients Died in America's Worst Drug Disaster*. Simon & Schuster.

(4)   Vandenbroucke, J. and Psaty, B.M. (2009) Benefits and risks of drug treatment; how to combine the best evidence on benefits with the best data about adverse effects. *JAMA 300: 2417-2419.*

(5)   Hux, J.E. and Naylor, C.D. (1995) Does the Format of Efficacy Data Determine Patients' Acceptance of Treatment? *Medical Decision Making 15: 152-157.*

(6)   Malenka, D.J. et al (1993) The Framing Effects of Absolute and Relative Risk. *J. Gen. Int. Med 8*: *543-548*.

(7)   Fahey, T. et al (1995) Evidence-based Purchasing. *BMJ* 311: *1056-1060*.

(8)   NICE (2008) *Social Value Judgements*. NICE. http://www.nice.org.uk/media/C18/30/SVJ2PUBLICATION 2008.pdf ; accessed 9/04/2009

(9)   Gray, J.A.M. and Porter, T. (2009) Opportunity Value *JHSRP 14: 129-130*.

(10)   Pearson, S.D. and Rawlins, M.D. (2005) Quality, Innovation and Value for Money: NICE and the British National Health Service. *JAMA 294: 2618-2622*.

(11)   Chalmers, I. (2007) The Alzheimer's Society, Drug Companies and Public Trust. *BMJ 335: 400*.

(12)   Newdick, C. (2008) *Priority Setting: Legal Considerations*. The NHS Confederation.

(13)   Austin, D. (2008) *Priority Setting: Managing Individual Funding Requests*. The NHS Confederation.

Question 6: Are the patients most likely to benefit from the interventions, and least likely to be harmed by them, clearly defined?

This section will:

- review the various types of drift;
- explain how the patients seen by a clinical service often have different characteristics from the patients treated in research studies;
- introduce the concept that cost-effectiveness is reduced as the threshold for treatment changes;
- consider the role of the clinician in individualising evidence.

By the end of this section you will have an understanding of:

- the different factors that result in an intervention shown to do more good than harm for one group of patients being offered to other patients who are not the same as the original group;
- how to describe the law of diminishing returns;
- what is meant by the 'overuse' of a technology;
- how to describe personalised medicine, and how to distinguish it from precision medicine.

The simplest answer is that the patients most likely to benefit are those whose clinical condition is exactly the same as that of the patients in the research which produced the evidence leading to the decision to introduce the treatment. For example, the Abatacept trial found that the drug was effective in patients with rheumatoid arthritis who had an 'inadequate response to Methotrexate'. Thus, only patients with an inadequate response to Methotrexate should be given Abatacept. (1) Once the intervention becomes widely used, however, adherence to these criteria is not always strictly observed and the criteria often drift, which may be driven by clinicians, patients, or industry, or all three. Clinicians will always try to do more for their patients and may try a drug even if the patient is not exactly the same as the patients in the research, but there are other factors that cause drift.

Drift from growth

'Don't let those bloody physicians get their hands on the kidney!' This was the only advice I received from the head of the Department of Surgery when I started work as a junior doctor. To my surprise, I had discovered that the Department of Surgery was responsible for acute dialysis for their region, and that I was not only one of the team that would run it, but also that, when the only other member of the team, a Senior Registrar of great experience and competence, went off to operate in another city, I was the team!

And so we dialysed! Almost every night, when the day job was finished, we wheeled out the kidney, a silver cylinder about the size of a dustbin, filled it with water from the tap, turned on the heating element, poured in bags of sodium chloride, glucose, and other mixers in smaller amounts, and stirred the mixture with what is known in Scotland as a 'spurtle' – a wooden stick with a thistle carved at the top for stirring porridge – until the salts dissolved, and the solution was warm enough. At this point we connected the patient to the machine, wrote up the night's plan, and went to bed, perchance to sleep! It was a very successful service.

When resources are as limited as they were when there was one artificial kidney for a million people, the decision to dialyse was not difficult. In a small number of patients, acute renal failure is temporary, and if they are supported for a period of time, kidney function is regained and patients no longer need dialysis. The introduction of a single artificial kidney to a population that does not have one, therefore, adds great value. Young people, who would probably have died before the arrival of the kidney dialysis machine, do not die. I say 'probably' because some people recover kidney function spontaneously and some of our 'successes' were not attributable to our activity as doctors, although the patients always gave us the credit.

Imagine now that the number of artificial kidneys was increased from one to ten. The indications for dialysis would change: in addition to dialysing only young fit people with a high chance of recovery, other older, less fit patients with more severe kidney disease or with other health problems would be accepted for dialysis. There would be some increase in value, but it would not be tenfold. Imagine now that the number of kidneys for transplant were increased from 10 to 50. The same phenomenon would be observed, illustrating the Law of Diminishing Returns.

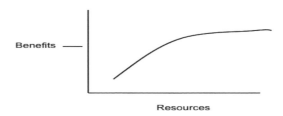

Figure Question 6.1 The Law of Diminishing Returns

Technology-driven drift

As diagnostic tests become less uncomfortable, they are used on more patients. CT scanning, for example, is less uncomfortable and less risky than the insertion of catheters into arteries for conventional x-ray, so it is judged appropriate to investigate people whose symptoms are less severe.

Drift can also occur if technology reduces risk. As the adverse effects of treatments diminish, for example as laparoscopic ('keyhole') surgery replaces open surgery for removal of the gall bladder, clinicians and patients may accept an operation which they would not previously have done. As the risk of surgery decreases, more people are judged to be 'fit for surgery', so the number of operations with a lower relative risk increases, but the absolute number of deaths remains constant.

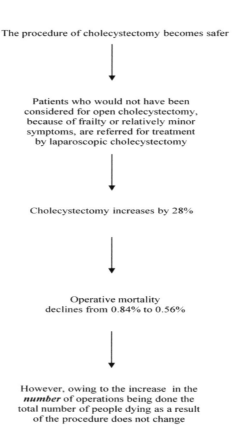

The procedure of cholecystectomy becomes safer

Patients who would not have been
considered for open cholecystectomy,
because of frailty or relatively minor
symptoms, are referred for treatment
by laparoscopic cholecystectomy

Cholecystectomy increases by 28%

Operative mortality
declines from 0.84% to 0.56%

However, owing to the increase in the
number of operations being done the
total number of people dying as a result
of the procedure does not change

Figure 6.2 The impact of changing the threshold for an operation

As care becomes better organised and of better quality, often as a
result of the development of specialist centres, the risks associated
with treatment fall, and patients who were previously considered to be
too unwell for treatment are reclassified as eligible for treatment.

Patient-driven drift

> *'I operated on the cataract of the retired professor of pathology. He was delighted. His golf handicap dropped by 2. In the following two months, five other members of his golf club were referred for cataract surgery.'*
> (Consultant Ophthalmologist)

When cataract surgery was first introduced, the results were amazing. People with very little vision, some even registered blind, were operated on. As the capacity for cataract surgery increased, the criteria for operation changed. People with less severe degrees of visual loss had their cataracts removed. The cataract operation entered common knowledge, and among older people, demand grew and the early strict criteria started to drift. Patient demands increase as interventions become less unpleasant or less risky.

Industry driven drift

Individual companies try to increase market share, but an industry as a whole may lobby for a particular condition or treatment to be given priority. Direct advertising of a drug or product is one obvious method. In countries in which 'direct to consumer' advertising of drugs is not allowed, healthcare industries – either alone or in concert – have started to fund patient groups, campaigning for more resources for a particular health need, such as female incontinence or osteoporosis. In addition, celebrities who have personal experience of a disease, either as patients or carers, may be recruited to act as figureheads, thus attracting press interest.

From under-use to over-use – reducing inappropriate clinical practice

Healthcare interventions can be classified as being either necessary or discretionary. Necessary interventions are those over which there is no debate, for example:

- treatment of acute appendicitis, or
- stabilisation of a fractured femur.

The decision about whether or not to intervene is straightforward, provided that the necessary resources are available. Discretionary interventions are those in which the decision whether or not to intervene rests with the doctor and the patient. Examples of this are:

- psychotherapy;
- repair of damaged ligaments in people who are not engaged in professional sport;
- admission to hospital of patients with heart failure.

When a new technology or service of proven benefit is introduced, it is usually under-used. This can be defined as a failure to provide the service or technology to those patients who have the same characteristics as the patients in the trial from which the evidence emerged that led to the decision to introduce the service. The increased investment of resources to provide the service to all such patients will be of value, (although how much value depends, of course, on the other needs that could be met with those resources). There will come a point in time when all the patients who have the same characteristics as the patients in the trial are receiving the service. This can be described as the optimum level of use of the technology.

When it is judged that there is over-use of technology, the adjective 'inappropriate' is often used, but inappropriateness is a value judgement. For payers and providers of care, variations in the rate of interventions are an indicator of over- and under-use, and the *Annual Report* of England's Chief Medical Officer for 2005 contained a whole chapter on the need to tackle variation, entitled 'Waste Not, Want Not'. (2) Over-use at a population level results from what is called inappropriate clinical practice, but it is very difficult for clinicians to know that they are being inappropriate when face to face with a patient.

The appropriateness of care provided to an individual patient or group of patients can be determined in several different ways:

- by asking an independent clinician or group of clinicians to pass judgement on the intervention given;
- by comparing the intervention given to a patient with clinical guidelines indicating which patients are most likely to benefit, or are least likely to be harmed, by that intervention;

- by using a validated tool, such as a Patient Reported Outcome Measure, to assess health status before the intervention.

As the distinction between appropriateness and inappropriateness is a matter of judgement, there is a spectrum of potential categories. In many studies of appropriateness, three categories are identified:

- clearly appropriate;
- clearly inappropriate
- a class in between where clinicians, experts and patients disagree, depending upon their values

The concept of appropriateness is particularly useful when making decisions about what Naylor has called the 'grey zones of clinical practice', namely aspects of care for which the evidence is scarce, or the evidence available is not relevant to the patient or the service under consideration. (3)

One way to identify inappropriate care is to look for variations in the amount of care provided. This was first studied by Jack Wennberg and his colleagues at Dartmouth Medical School who published an Atlas (4) showing that there was no variation for conditions in which the judgement and choice of clinicians and patients were unimportant – fractured neck of femur, for example – whereas there were great variations for interventions in which judgement played a part in the decision – knee replacement, for example. Furthermore, the clinicians and the patients who were in populations in which there were three times as many operations did not know there were three times as many operations and that a higher proportion of operations were inappropriate.

Is this patient likely to benefit?

Research produces evidence that in a sample of patients with certain characteristics in common, all being aged under 65 for example, a treatment is more likely to do good than harm. The first priority of a health service that has decided to fund this treatment is that all the people in their population with the same characteristics as those in the research should be offered the treatment. However, because the researchers chose their sample based on strict criteria only a proportion of the people with the disease are exactly like those in the research report, many will be over 65 for example, or have other diseases. The job of the clinician is to relate the research findings to the unique individual patient, taking into account their clinical condition and, in discussion with them, ascertaining the values they attach to the outcomes, both good and bad, of the treatment.

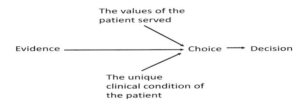

Figure Question 6.3 Individualising evidence

The difficulty of doing this is not to be underestimated but it is a task, now called 'personalised medicine' (5) that clinicians have to do many times each day. In good clinical practice clinicians often give a treatment to an individual patient who is not exactly the same as the patients in the research and those who pay for care have to accept that this happens, but if the clinician identifies new groups of patients which they deem need treatment the payer is justified in trying to control the change in practice.

The importance of engaging patients in this process was also a consequence of the appreciation of the fact that one reason why variation occurred was that the values of the individual patient were not being taken into account. This led Jack Wennberg, Al Mulley and Mike Barry to develop tools for shared decision-making – these will be used in the spirit of the NHS White Paper's principle of:

'Nothing about me without me.'

Furthermore, the use of tools called PROMS (Patent Reported Outcome Measures) will allow the service to ensure that the service is measuring outcomes, not process.

Questions for reflection when teaching or developing networks

If using these in network building or teaching, give one of the questions to the group and ask them to work in pairs to reflect on the question for three minutes; try to get people who do not know one another to work together.

When taking feedback, let each pair make only one point. In the interests of equity, if you start with the pair on the left-hand side of the room for the first question, start with the pair on the right-hand side of the room for the second question.

- How can those who pay for healthcare prevent or reduce drift?
- When is a clinician justified in using a treatment for a patient who is not exactly like the type of patient in the research studies which demonstrated that the treatment does more good than harm?
- What are the principal barriers to personalised medicine?

References

(1)   Kremer, J.L. et al (2006) Effects of Abatacept in Patients with Methotrexate-resistant Active Rheumatoid Arthritis. *Ann. Int. Med. 144: 865-876.*

(2)   Donaldson, Sir Liam (2006) *On the State of the Public Health: Annual Report Of The CMO 2005.* Department of Health.

(3)   Naylor, C.D. (1995) The Grey Zones of Clinical Practice. *Lancet 345: 840-842.*

(4)   Wennberg, J. (1998) *The Dartmouth Atlas of Healthcare.* American Hospital Publishing.

(5)   Rothwell, P.M. (2008) Treating Individuals: from Randomised Trials to Personalised Medicine. *Blackwell.*

Question 7: Is effectiveness being maximised?

This section will:

- examine the difference in benefits and harms likely to be seen in a research setting and an ordinary service setting;
- examine the need to introduce new services carefully to maximise benefits and minimise harms;
- introduce the need for systems of care to be created;
- review the relevance of quality assurance to value improvement.

By the end of this chapter you will have an understanding of:

- the importance of planning the introduction of new services or interventions to minimise the gap between the ordinary service setting and the research setting;
- the key elements of a healthcare system;
- how to set and re-set standards of care.

People who manage healthcare resources, most of whom are clinicians, are not usually involved in answering the first three of the value questions:

- How much money should be spent on healthcare?
- How much money should be spent on research and education?
- How should money be allocated to different populations?

People who manage healthcare are involved in decisions to allocate resources to different groups of patients because the force of their argument, often reflecting the power of the clinicians in that specialty, influences resource allocation. They are also closely involved with payers in deciding what resources and interventions should be provided for a particular group of patients, and which types of patients are most likely to benefit from those interventions – the fourth, fifth and sixth value questions. The final four questions are primarily the responsibility of people who manage healthcare, although the introduction of 'pay for performance' has brought policy makers and payers much more into the quality debate.

Those who manage healthcare now have their own set of questions to answer if they are to live up to the 20th century proverb that management consists of two tasks: 'Doing the right things, and doing them right.' The modern manager must be able to answer, both to their payer, and to the patients and populations they serve, questions 7, 8, 9, and 10:

- Is the effectiveness of care being maximised?
- Are the risks of care being minimised?
- Can costs be reduced further without increasing harm or reducing benefit?
- Could each patient's experience be improved?

The 21st century has added a twist to the old proverb because managers are not only expected to do things right, they are expected to do things better and better each year and answer the supplementary questions:

- Are we doing better than last year?
- How do we plan to do even better next year?

Choose the right things to do

The first step in maximising effectiveness is to introduce only those interventions for which there is strong evidence that they will do more good than harm. However, the effectiveness of a health service – 'the degree to which attainable improvements in health are, in fact, attained' (1) – is achieved not only by deciding to provide interventions for which there is strong research evidence of benefit (that is, answering question 5 correctly), but also by ensuring that the benefit demonstrated in the research project which produced the evidence leading to the decision to introduce the service, is actually reproduced in practice. The second step in maximising effectiveness is, therefore, to introduce only new interventions that are within the capacity of the service to deliver.

Ensure the right things can be done well in an ordinary service setting

The magnitude of the benefit demonstrated in the research setting is sometimes called the efficacy of an intervention, but research is usually done by people who:

- are highly committed;
- have special interest and expertise;
- work to highly defined protocols;
- have their performance continually measured;
- have resources earmarked for the work.

In the busy service setting, however, these advantages do not exist, and the quality of care may be lower, which means that the magnitude of benefit is lower (Figure Q7.1).

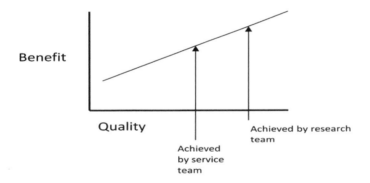

Figure Question 7.1 The difference between the quality of service and research settings

It is, therefore, not enough to answer question 5 (are the interventions being offered all likely to confer a good balance of benefit and harm?). Particularly when being pressed by an enthusiastic clinician, keen to introduce a new operation or service about which he has either read about or heard of at a conference, it is also essential to ask:

- does this service have, or could it develop, the skills and resources to achieve a level of quality high enough to produce sufficient benefit to justify the investment of resources?

If it is not possible to achieve this level of quality, it does not make sense to introduce the service. Some interventions are easier to introduce, with the confidence that the amount of benefit shown in research can be reproduced. The introduction of a new statin, which would lower cholesterol more effectively, is relatively easy. The introduction of a new surgical operation, requiring high levels of skill and long experience, or a screening programme, requiring high levels of programme management, is much more challenging. (2) To manage the introduction of new services in this way requires:

- a system for deciding whether or not to introduce new technology;
- a system for managing the introduction of new services if a decision to introduce them is taken;
- the publication of standards that service providers are expected to achieve.

To ensure that the outcomes demonstrated in the research setting are reproduced in practice, it is essential to set explicit standards, and in *Equity and Excellence* it is emphasised that the National Institute for Clinical Excellence will 'develop authoritative standards setting out each part of the patient pathway'.

When services are in place, it is then necessary to ensure that each improves year after year after year, and this is done by:

- creating a system of care and making the pathways and key decision points explicit, using the 'Map of Medicine' software which allows care pathways, with links to the evidence, to be displayed and localised to take into account local constraints and opportunities;
- comparing the performance of each service against explicit standards;
- helping each service improve their performance;
- resetting the standards regularly.

This is the process of continuous quality improvement.

Creating systems

A system is a set of activities with a common set of objectives. Each service must have both a broad aim and a set of objectives. The aim of the NHS Abdominal Aortic Aneurysm Programme, for example, was defined as being to reduce the mortality from rupture of the aorta. Its specific objectives were defined as follows.

- To offer all men screening in the year following their 65th birthday.
- To ensure that men accepting or refusing screening had an accurate understanding of the benefits and risks involved.
- To measure the abdominal aortic diameter accurately in two dimensions, using designated ultrasound machines.
- To provide continuing surveillance for men whose aortic diameter is over 30mm but less than 55mm.
- To refer all men with an aortic diameter in excess of 55mm to a centre that is part of a nationally recognised network.
- To minimise anxiety and harm.
- To provide support for staff involved in the programme.
- To be accountable to the population served.
- To promote and support research.

For each objective, one or more outcome criteria must be chosen in order to allow progress, or the lack of it, to be measured.

Comparing the service with other services

In requiring managers to do better year after year, it necessary to be clear about the yardstick. It is obviously meritorious for a service to do better than it did the previous year, but that is not sufficiently rigorous because a service could improve from being 'very dangerous' to being 'dangerous'. It is essential for a service to compare itself with other services. Fortunately, the term 'average' has come to have a meaning that implies value, as well as its original statistical meaning, and for a service to boast that it was 'above average' would impress few patients or payers. Furthermore, the average level of performance could be unacceptably poor, and 'above average' could also be unacceptable. For this reason, performance has to be compared with standards.

Comparing the system with standards

'The quality of a health service is the degree to which it conforms to pre-set standards of goodness.' Avedis Donabedian

Standards are subjective. They are value statements. What the manager regards as a good quality service may be regarded as one of very poor quality by the patient, or vice versa. A patient may regard the service as one of very high quality, whereas the payer may regard it as of unacceptably low quality. One reason for this is that each may be considering different aspects of the service, each of which has a quality, and different organisations describe the aspects of the service in different ways, although there are similarities. The best way to set standards is to decide, on the basis of levels of performance described in the research reports and, if available, data from other services, what would be:

- a minimum acceptable standard, below which no service should be allowed to operate;
- an achievable standard to which all services can aspire, and which some will easily surpass (Figure Q7.2).

Figure Question 7.2 Different levels of quality

Regular resetting of standards for continuous improvement

If standards are not being changed annually, it is proof they are not being used. Kauro Ishikawa: Total Quality Control – The Japanese Way

Part of quality assurance is the regular resetting of standards, to prevent boredom and complacency, even though providers may complain about the constant shifting of the goalposts (Figure Q7.3).

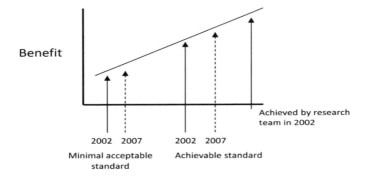

Figure Question 7.3 The re-setting of standards, showing how the achievable standard of the service approaches excellence.

The use of the methods of continuous quality improvement leads to steady improvement in performance. All services have to be involved in a process of continuous quality improvement, until the payer decides that the added value of further improvement of a service is less valuable than the investment of resources in another service.

Questions for reflection when teaching or developing networks

If using these in network building or teaching, give one of the questions to the group and ask them to work in pairs to reflect on the question for three minutes; try to get people who do not know one another to work together.

When taking feedback, let each pair make only one point. In the interests of equity, if you start with the pair on the left-hand side of the room for the first question, start with the pair on the right-hand side of the room for the second question.

- What aspects of an innovation would lead you to decide that careful preparation and planning was needed before its introduction?
- Of services currently offered, which ones are delivered as systems?
- In this section, minimal acceptable, achievable and excellent standard are described; what other levels of standard could be chosen?

References

(1)   Donabedian, A. (2002) *An Introduction To Quality Assurance In Healthcare*. Oxford University Press.

(2)   Meakins, J. and Gray, J.A.M. (2005) *Evidence-Based Surgery*. Surgical Clinics of North America.

Question 8: Are clinical risks being minimised?

This section will:

- review the different causes of harm;
- explore the relationship between quality and safety.

By the end of this chapter you will have an understanding of:

- the causes of harm in healthcare;
- the distinction between harm caused by poor quality and harm caused by medical error;
- how harm reduces value.

'Punters, we just call them punters, because – let's face it – they are taking a chance every time they use the health service!'

A punter is someone who takes a gamble. In a debate at a serious meeting in Belfast about what the people who use health services should be called – patients or consumers – the term 'punter' was the sensible suggestion of one of the doctors. A punter, one who takes a gamble, is a serious and respectful term.

All healthcare can cause harm. Everyone who uses health services runs the risk of harm, but this harm affects not only the patient but also clinicians, managers, and payers. Harm reduces value. There are two types of harm:

- harm caused by doing the wrong thing – errors;
- harm caused by doing the right thing badly – quality problems.

Cutting off the wrong leg is an error; cutting off the correct leg, but doing it so badly that the patient needs a second operation, is harm from poor quality care. The harm that results from poor quality healthcare, and the harm that results from errors are, however, inter-related, because errors are less likely to occur in high quality services.(1)

Harm caused by doing the right thing badly

Because both benefit and this type of harm are functions of the quality of care provided, the higher the quality of care the better the balance between benefit and harm. There is also a level of quality at which the harms are greater than the benefits. At this point – the minimal acceptable level of quality – the service should be stopped. (See Figure 7.2)

Harm caused by doing the wrong things – errors

An operation on the wrong side of the body, or the prescription of a drug to which the patient is known to be allergic, are errors. Some errors will always occur, but the number of errors can be minimised.

Preventing errors by continuous quality improvement

Services become high quality for a number of reasons, many of which are factors which have been shown to reduce the incidence of errors, notably:

- good leadership;
- development of systems;
- the creation of a strong culture.

To maximise the probability of benefit and minimise the probability of harm and errors, professionals need 'Standard Operating Procedures' (SOPs), defined in Wikipedia on 3 August 2006 as *'a procedure, or set of procedures, to perform a given operation or evolution in reaction to a specific event.'* The NHS in England and Wales is now using software, called The Map of Medicine, to depict those pathways and SOPs explicitly.

In his annual report for 2005, The Chief Medical Officer (CMO) for England, Professor Sir Liam Donaldson, emphasised the need for SOPs. (2) He said that SOPs had a major contribution to make to patient safety, but he recognised that SOPs – 'doing everything exactly the same way all the time' – was 'counter-cultural in healthcare.' By that, he meant counter to the culture of clinical autonomy. The challenge was illustrated by the story of an encounter with a surgeon, who told Sir Liam: 'If you introduce that approach, it will be like working in a factory, not being a doctor.' The CMO replied robustly that there is now evidence from many specialties that SOPs are 'compatible with high quality clinical practice by highly trained, highly skilled professionals who continue to exercise judgement in vast areas of their practice.'

Preventing errors by targeted programmes

To improve quality and safety, it is necessary to have a style of general management which will increase effectiveness and reduce harm, for example:

- promotion of safety culture;
- use of systems, including SOPs;
- clear lines of accountability for risk management and safety;
- data collection about risk factors, errors and near misses.

It is also necessary to have risk management, targeting those activities or environments where errors are most common and serious, for example:

- high risk activities:
  - prescribing;
  - handover of care from one clinician to another;
  - patient identification;
- high risk areas:
  - intensive care;
  - operating theatres;
  - emergency departments.

In addition, when new hazards about adverse events and near misses are identified through research, or through the collection and analysis of data, the organisation needs to respond quickly and sensitively, meeting the concerns of the patient who has been harmed, and reducing the risk that other patients could be harmed in the same way. This is what many patients want when harm occurs. The 100,000 Lives Campaign of the Institute of Healthcare Improvement offers an excellent example of how the application of what is known but not done can have a major impact. (3)

Of central importance is a system for the identification of unsafe practice, or a service culture in which it is likely that errors and poor quality care will occur, and the White Paper, *Equity and Excellence: Liberating the NHS*, endorses the principle that patient feedback can provide early warnings of system failure.

Questions for reflection when teaching or developing networks

If using these in network building or teaching, give one of the questions to the group and ask them to work in pairs to reflect on the question for three minutes; try to get people who do not know one another to work together.

When taking feedback, let each pair make only one point. In the interests of equity, if you start with the pair on the left-hand side of the room for the first question, start with the pair on the right-hand side of the room for the second question.

- If you were reducing harm would you give priority to the prevention of error or improving quality?
- How could you most clearly explain on local radio that all healthcare causes harm?
- What is the best way to explain to patients the balance of benefit and harm?

References

(1)   Institute of Medicine (1999) *To Err is Human: Building Safer Health Systems*. National Academy Press.

(2)   Donaldson, L. (2006) *On the State of the Public Health: Annual Report of the Chief Medical Officer 2005*. Department of Health.

(3)   Berwick, D.M. (2006) The 100,000 Lives Campaign. *JAMA* 295: 324-7.

Question 9: Can costs be cut without increasing harm or reducing effectiveness?

This section will:

- review the terms used in describing the use of resources;
- introduce the concept of sustainability;
- examine the different techniques that can be used to reduce waste.

By the end of this chapter you will have an understanding of:

- the difference between efficiency and productivity;
- the principal causes of wasted resources;
- how to define sustainable healthcare;
- how increased productivity need not decrease the ability of a care provider to personalise care.

There are two ways in which costs can be cut:

- paying less for the resources, and
- extracting more value from the resources

Paying less for the resources

The procurement of drugs, buildings or equipment offers an opportunity for paying less and the most radical approach is called 'value-based pricing'. Traditionally the price of a drug has been based on the costs of its development. In value-based pricing the price is based on an 'assessment of whether the additional health expected to be gained from its use exceeds the health forgone as other health treatments are displaced by its additional cost'. There is support for this approach but 'the debate about…the meaning of value and the relationship between guidance, price value and evidence is however very much alive.' (1) This important paper was written in 2008 and in 2010 the Government, in its White Paper, *Equity and Excellence:*

Liberating the NHS, gave a commitment that 'we will pay drug companies according to the value of new resources'.

Extracting more value from the resources

After a business dinner with good food, plentiful drink and bonhomie, it is usually time for a welcome night's sleep. It was a different ending to the story, however, when, at a business dinner, Taiichi Ohno, the recently retired creator of the Toyota production system, finally agreed to advise an American company on how to reduce waste. Any thought of rest was postponed! To the host's 'See you in the morning!' Ohno replied that, if they were serious, they should make an immediate start: call in staff, reorganise the production line, ignore the possible protests of unions. This they did. Ohno moved from the dinner table to the shop floor – jackets off, sleeves up, machinery moved, waste slashed, and productivity increased. (2)

The Japanese term *kaizen*, meaning continual gradual improvement, is now part of the management vocabulary. The term *muda*, meaning waste, is less well-known. Ohno hated waste, defined as 'any human activity which consumes resources but produces no value.' Taiichi Ohno, who has been called the most ferocious hater of waste in history, described seven categories of waste in industrial systems and listed them as:

- over-production;
- waiting time;
- transportation;
- wasteful processing;
- too much stock;
- too much movement in the factory floor;
- defective products.

Ohno's work, and his concept of 'lean thinking' which flowed from it, is of central importance to those who pay for, or manage, health services, but there are some important differences about healthcare, in particular the need to distinguish between productivity and efficiency.(3)

Good outcomes and high productivity are not mutually exclusive

The outcome of healthcare can only be measured by examining and listening to patients. Examples of good outcomes are:

- survival;
- cure;
- reduced disability.

Efficiency relates the outcomes of what economists call the Inputs, which can be money, staff, beds or other resources. Efficiency is calculated by the formula:

$$Efficiency = \frac{Outcomes}{Inputs}$$

Figure Question 9.1 Efficiency

Productivity is simpler to measure. It relates the process of care, the Outputs in the economists' terms, to the Inputs. Productivity is calculated by the formula:

$$Productivity = \frac{Outputs}{Inputs}$$

Figure Question 9.2 Productivity

The efficiency of a cataract service is demonstrated by the number of people able to drive again after cataract removal. The productivity is the number of cataract operations per bed.

The outcomes of care are determined by the interventions used and the quality of the service provided, and resources are wasted if a service is not using the:

- right interventions to treat the
- right patients in the
- right way.

The seven steps to improve productivity

Those who pay for and manage the service that is doing the right things, to the right patients, can address the seven causes of low productivity in health services:

1. under-use of buildings and equipment;
2. too much stock;
3. too much cost for non-essential non-clinical staff;
4. too much wasted time, for clinicians <u>and</u> patients;
5. care in hospital instead of at home;
6. staff too skilled, and scarce for the task in hand;
7. equipment and tools of unnecessary expense.

A question, and answer, for each cause is offered below.

(1)   Can we make more use of buildings and equipment?

'Sweat the assets' is an industrial proverb, meaning use buildings and plant to the maximum.

- Many Health Centres in the United Kingdom are shut for 115.5 hours in the week.

- Many MRI machines are not used for more than one third of the time.

Staff, of course, have rights, but if a smaller proportion of staff worked from 8.00 a.m. to 6.00 p.m. five days a week, much greater use could be made of fixed assets.

(2)   Can we carry less stock?

In 2005, 574 different head and socket combinations were used in (hip replacement) operations in England and Wales. It seems implausible that meaningful data can be gathered, or that money can be saved through bulk purchase, when such a number of products and supplies is used in this way. Annual Report of the Chief Medical Officer for England, 2005

Just-in-time delivery of the equipment needed was one of the great achievements of the Toyota Productions Systems. Most health services buy:

- too much equipment of
- too many types, and

- store it for too long.

Such waste can be prevented, and cured, by better procurement.

(3) How can we reduce the cost of essential non-clinical staff?

Clinical staff see patients, or samples of patients. They need technical staff, catering, supplies, and laundry, and they need administration and management staff. Different approaches have been taken to reduce costs, for example:

- outsourcing of non-clinical services to reduce staff costs, because many private contractors pay lower wages or provide less benefits than public service employers, can be viewed as a moral, as well as a productivity issue;
- reducing the number of tasks that administrative staff have to do, for example by reducing demands for data;
- reducing the number of management staff;
- reorganisation.

Of these methods, the last appears the least effective, and may increase costs in both the short- and the long-term. The simplest approach is to reduce the work that non-clinical staff do and their numbers. The White Paper, *Equity and Excellence: Liberating the NHS*, both identifies the '260,000 returns made annually to the Department of Health' as the work that needs to be cut unless it improves value, and states that 'the Government will reduce management costs by at least 45%'.

(4) Can the waste of clinician and patient time be reduced?

Time is the scarcest resource for clinicians. For most clinicians, the highest value work time is that spent on clinical work, followed by research, and then education.

Some of the 'other activities' may have high value, for example if a physician is reimbursed for half a day to reward the time spent in managing resources but much is, in the everyday phrase, a waste of time, examples of which are:

- meetings without purpose or conclusion;

- looking for lost notes or data;
- getting a new identity card or parking space.

All clinicians have their own lists of what they consider to be a waste of time, but their valuations may not be shared. Attendance at a management meeting may be classified as a waste of time by the clinician, but regarded as high value by a manager. It would require independent evaluation to determine whether the clinician was correct, and the meeting was unfocused and unproductive, or whether the manager's perspective, that the clinician came to a good meeting with the wrong attitude, was correct. Education and research can also be unproductive and of low value. Education is of low value if:

- it is not determined by the formally ascertained learning needs of the clinician, as opposed to their wants. There is evidence that if clinicians are interested in a topic and want to learn, they will seek out the learning they need. Expenditure on formal training should be reserved for topics for which the clinician is not delivering good quality care;
- it is not delivered using methods which have evidence of effectiveness; large lectures are usually of low value.

Research is of low value if:

- the answer is already known;
- the design is inappropriate or inadequate;
- the conduct of the research is sloppy;
- the reporting is biased.

Clinical practice is of high value, but within the course of clinical work the time of clinicians and patients is often wasted, if:

- the patient's notes are missing;
- key data, such as laboratory results, are not available;
- there is unnecessary waiting time, such as between operations in a theatre.

(5)   Is care being delivered in the most appropriate place?

Many patients are treated in facilities which have levels of staffing and equipment which they do not need.

- 'Bed blockers' are patients, usually elderly, who have recovered from the acute phase of their disease but cannot be discharged because they are now too disabled to return home but are unable to be placed in a nursing home. This is a matter of concern both for those who manage or pay for care, and for the patients themselves who are at high risk of hospital-acquired infection, institutionalisation, and malnutrition.
- Patients who attend a clinic with a problem that might have been resolved if their primary care clinician could have phoned, emailed, or had other means of accessing the expertise of the specialist.
- People who die in hospital who could die at home with support.

The 'Five Whys?' of Taiichi Ohno are worth asking frequently in healthcare.

(6) Could this care be provided by less highly trained staff?

Highly trained staff are scarce, and it is a waste of their time to carry out tasks which could be managed equally well by staff who have not had the training to carry out all the tasks of the highly skilled person, but who have been trained specifically to carry out a finite range of tasks. Sometimes such staff carry out repetitive tasks with greater attention to detail, and with better results than the most highly trained staff to whom such tasks are, at best, boring or, at worst, a waste of time.

(7) Can we procure good equipment and drugs cheaper?

When asked what passed through his mind the minute before take-off, the astronaut replied: 'I could not stop thinking that I am sitting on top of the cheapest tender!'

Some people prefer the term 'low cost' to 'cheap', and 'lower cost' to 'cheaper', but who cares about the niceties of language, the key question is why pay more than is necessary? Costs can be reduced by:

- skilful procurement;

- bulk purchase;
- the use of generic rather than branded drugs;
- sometimes 'making' rather than 'buying'.

These activities are ethically important because they reduce waste, increase productivity, and release resources for clinical care. In a significant policy commitment in the White Paper, *Equity and Excellence: Liberating the NHS*, published in July 2010, the government stated that 'we will pay drug companies according to the value of new medicines.'

Beyond large-scale production

This is the subtitle of Taiichi Ohno's short (143 pages) classic on *The Toyota Production System* (4) emphasising that one of the cleverest things that Kiichiro Toyoda, the President, and Ohno did was not to overtake the Ford Motor Company with even larger scale production but by small scale production, with less stock and less waste and more flexibility. This not only made good sense but allowed the company to evolve by customer pull, rather than by factory push. Toyota makes personalised cars when an order is placed, so combining industrial production methods and personalisation can lead to success in the manufacturing industry, and also in healthcare. Becoming more productive does not mean becoming less personal.

'Beyond large-scale production' is what is called 'mass automisation' as epitomised by Dell Computers or the Mini, where the benefits of mass production are combined with the involvement of the customer in selecting which mass-produced parts it wishes to have combined to make a unique product. The analogy is that the evidence and the guidelines are mass-produced and then personalised by the clinician.

Sustainable Healthcare

The War on Waste is justified by the need to reduce costs that are not essential for the care of patients. The War has now a second justification – the need for greener healthcare.

The carbon footprint of a health service will be a standard quality metric by the year 2015. For many people paying for or managing healthcare, the term 'waste' has been synonymous with refuse, and the disposal of refuse has come up the management agenda because of the increased costs of refuse disposal. The rising cost of energy has also made managers energy conscious but only for short term financial reasons. By 2015, at the latest, these issues will be seen not only as financial issues but also as a moral issue and a health issue, because the health consequences of environmental change will have as big an impact on the health of the population in the 21st century as smoking had on the 20th century. (5)

Every service should know the size of its carbon footprint and have a plan to shrink it. Productivity relates the outputs of a health service to its direct costs, sustainability relates the outputs to the life cycle costs of its resources which include the costs of manufacturing and waste disposal. Sustainability is the new dimension of quality and it will become as dominant as effectiveness or equity.

The work done by the Centre for Sustainable Healthcare demonstrated that the principal source of healthcare carbon was not the heating and lighting of buildings but clinical care – staff and patient travel, drugs and equipment.(6) Sustainable clinical practice is a style of clinical work in which:

- every clinician tries to prevent disease;
- the patient is at the centre, the co-ordinating point, preventing unknowing duplication;
- pathways are as lean as possible, with unnecessary follow-ups cancelled, for example;
- the clinician's treatment choices have all had their carbon cost assessed and minimised.

Carbon is the new currency of healthcare.

Questions for reflection when teaching or developing networks

If using these in network building or teaching, give one of the questions to the group and ask them to work in pairs to reflect on the question for three minutes; try to get people who do not know one another to work together.

When taking feedback, let each pair make only one point. In the interests of equity, if you start with the pair on the left-hand side of the room for the first question, start with the pair on the right-hand side of the room for the second question.

- What are the principal sources of waste in a hospital?
- What are the principal sources of waste in the relationship between primary and secondary care?
- How could staff be best motivated to reduce the carbon footprint of the care they provide?

References

(1) Claxton, K. et al (2008) Value-based pricing for NHS drugs: an opportunity not to be missed. *BMJ* 336: 251-25.

(2) Liker, J. (2004) *The Toyota Way.* McGraw-Hill.

(3) Womack, J.P. and Jones, D.T. (1996) *Lean Thinking.* Simon & Schuster.

(4) Ohno, T. (1995) *The Toyota Production System.* Productivity Press.

(5) NHS Sustainable Development Unit (2009) *Reducing Carbon, Improving Health.* Department of Health. http://www.sdu.nhs.uk/page.php?area_id=2 accessed 9/04/2009

(6) Mortimer, F. (2010) The sustainable physician. *Clinical Medicine.* 10:110-111.

Question 10: Could each patient's experience be improved?

> **This section will:**
>
> - review the determinants of a patient's experience;
> - consider how the value a patient places on care may differ from the values of the professional;
> - discuss how outcomes of value can be measured.
>
> **By the end of this section you will have an understanding of:**
>
> - the difference between patient satisfaction and an assessment of the patient's experience for quality improvement;
> - the interplay of the different determinants of a patient's experience;
> - how experience can be measured.

To the clinician, the management of disease becomes, to some extent, routine. To the patient, the experience is unique and dramatic, with both clinically significant and insignificant incidents etched on memory. Three types of experience have been described, each distinct but all inter-related.

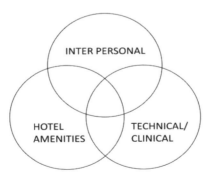

Figure Question 10 The factors which determine the patient's experience

The hotel experience

Hotel factors, such as food and car parking, can be judged by every patient, who will use as their yardstick a hotel they know, or a business they have visited. However, it is difficult for hospitals that accept all comers, planned admissions and emergencies, to give the appearance of calm prosperity exuded by hotels. Hospitals that specialise only in planned or elective care can maintain or acquire the atmosphere of a good hotel, with flowers, and carpets on the floor, but in a busy general hospital it is more difficult to disguise what it is – a place where life and death, conflict and drama, violence and sorrow, vomit and blood, are on stage day and night.

As a result of the increasing incidence of hospital-acquired infections, one hotel factor of great importance is cleanliness. Using the patient's experience to monitor cleanliness, and patient pressure to improve overt cleanliness, contributes to the prevention of hospital-acquired infections. With the exception of cleanliness, hotel factors are not a major determinant of patients' rating of the value of their care. If amenities such as car parking are unsatisfactory, they will annoy and irritate, but if they are excellent they will not necessarily lead to delight – people can put up with unappetising food, but rudeness and insensitivity are much more difficult to reconcile.

The inter-personal experience

Politeness is important but can cover a multitude of sins. The relationship between the respect shown to patients and the technical quality of care has not been clearly described but:

- it would not be unreasonable to expect a positive correlation between the technical quality of a service and the respect shown to patients, and one study published in the rigorous *New England Journal of Medicine* demonstrated that 'hospitals that provide a high level of patient satisfaction provided clinical care that was somewhat higher in quality for all the conditions examined'. [1]

- 'feeling respected as an individual' is an outcome that patients value highly and is of value in its own right, independent of the technical outcome of care.   Indeed for people with untreatable or incurable problems, it is the only outcome.

It is essential, therefore, to measure the patient's experience of the interpersonal aspects of care as well as measuring their hotel experience. Increasingly there is also interest in measuring the outcome of care from the patient's perspective.

The technical experience

Patients judge the technical quality of their care by the outcome, but high quality care does not necessarily guarantee good outcome. Some patients have a good outcome from poor quality care, and some patients have a bad outcome from good quality care.

Studies have shown that, not surprisingly, patients found it difficult to judge the technical quality of care. (2,3)   It is possible for patients to assess the quality of care, provided they have the opportunity to read the annual report of the service, and compare the data with reports of similar services, particularly if the report includes not only measures of activity but also outcomes of value to patients. (4)   However, individual patients rarely have access to this type of data at present and usually base their assessment on hotel and interpersonal aspects of their care. This will change, however, as outcomes of value to patients will be used by both those who pay for, and those who manage, care as routine measures of performance. In England, the Map of Medicine pathways, representing best value care, have been made available to patients through NHS Choices – www.nhs.uk.

Feedback on the experience of care is collected by a number of techniques, the revolution being initiated by the Picker Foundation which introduced surveys, and the use of the web now allows feedback of experience relating to an individual clinician, for example the service offered by www.iwantgreatcare.org

Measuring outcomes of value to patients

The outcomes of interest to clinicians and researchers have not always been identical to the outcomes of interest to patients (Figure Q10.2).

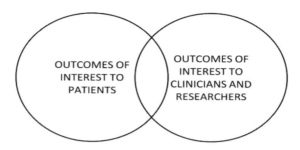

Figure Question 10.2 Outcomes of interest to patients

The involvement of patients in the design of research improves the quality and relevance of the research, by ensuring that outcomes of interest to patients are included in the study. Furthermore, it is sometimes possible to adopt, or adapt, the outcome measure employed in the research for use in routine clinical practice and healthcare management. It is also possible to give patients their care pathway, for example for the management of a chronic condition, not only so that they can be an even more effective co-ordinator of their care but also to clarify their responsibilities.

The use of PROMS, Patient Reported Outcome Measures, has become more popular as a means of measuring outcomes of importance to patients, and in the White Paper, *Equity and Excellence: Liberating the NHS*, there is a commitment that there will be 'much wider use of effective tools like PROMs, patient experience data and real time feedback' as part of the NHS Information Revolution.

Questions for reflection when teaching or developing networks

If using these in network building or teaching, give one of the questions to the group and ask them to work in pairs to reflect on the question for three minutes; try to get people who do not know one another to work together.

When taking feedback, let each pair make only one point. In the interests of equity, if you start with the pair on the left-hand side of the room for the first question, start with the pair on the right-hand side of the room for the second question.

- Is patient satisfaction of importance as an outcome of care?
- If you wanted to improve experience what aspect of care would you prioritise for improvement?
- How can patient experience be fed back to clinicians in a way most likely to change their behaviour?

References

(1)   Jha, K.A. et al (2008) Patients' perceptions of hospital care in the United States. *NEJM 359: 1321-1331.*

(2)   Chang, J.T. et al (2006) Patients' Global Ratings of their Healthcare are not Associated with the Technical Quality of their Care. *Ann. Int. Med. 144: 665-672.*

(3)   Rao, M. et al (2006) Patients' Own Assessment of Quality of Primary Care Compared with Objective Records Based on Measures of Technical Quality of Care. *BMJ 333: 19-22.*

(4)   Porter, M. and Teisberg, E. (2005) *Redefining Healthcare.* Harvard Business School Press.

5

THE BETTER VALUE HEALTHCARE TOOLKIT

This chapter will:

- present a structured approach to the analysis of tasks – Why? Who? When? How? – that can be used for any tasks;
- provide structured, brief guidance on common challenges rarely covered in management training.

By the end of this chapter you will have an understanding of how to tackle the following common challenges:

- responding to a bid for funding a new treatment;
- reviewing the allocation of resources between specialties or programmes;
- reviewing expenditure on a particular disease;
- coping with the torrent of knowledge;
- encouraging innovation;
- reviewing the scientific literature systematically;
- reducing the number of errors;
- improving patient experience;
- improving productivity;
- improving effectiveness;
- getting to the root of a problem;
- using IT for transformation.

No matter how senior you may be in the Royal Engineers, it is necessary always to carry with you a small notebook called *The Tactical Aide-Mémoire*. It contains all you must remember, the simple things that are so easy to forget when one gets more senior, partly because of age and partly because of familiarity with the task. *The Tactical Aide-Mémoire* helps ensure that the officer does not build a bridge that would not carry a tank or, even worse, not reach the other side of a ravine.

Based on this principle, we have developed a set of aides-mémoire for the manager or payer who is called upon to do the healthcare equivalent of throwing a bridge across a ravine.

WHAT?	*How to respond to a bid for a new treatment or service*
WHY?	Because management for better value requires tight control of innovation
WHO?	The person who holds the money, the clinician making the bid, and the person who manages their resources.
WHEN?	This can be done as part of the annual planning process or as new technologies emerge.
HOW?	<ul><li>The team that wants the new service should be asked to provide information about both the evidence-base and the relative value of the proposed innovation.<ul><li>Is the proposal based on a systematic review of the evidence?</li></ul></li><li>The bidder should be required to prepare a systematic review if one is not available. If the evidence-base is inadequate, the bidder can be encouraged to bid for research funds.</li><li>The bidder should provide data about:<ul><li>the number of patients in the group or population they service who would be helped and harmed by the new service;</li><li>how the benefits from the innovation compare with current service outcomes;</li><li>how the added benefits from the innovation compare with the added benefits that would result if the existing service were delivered at higher levels of quality.</li></ul></li><li>The relative value should be appraised, by asking the bidder to compare the value of this proposed addition to their service with:<ul><li>other innovations that the service might introduce in the next year;</li><li>the lowest value priority service they currently provide;</li><li>the problems that patients would face if some other part of the service were cut to fund this new service.</li></ul></li></ul>

WHAT?	*How to conduct an annual population value review*
WHY?	To ensure that resources are allocated between different budgets to maximise value and identify the need for movement of resources from one budget to another.
WHO?	People responsible for allocation of resources.
WHEN?	In the middle of the financial year, when expenditure for the previous year is clear and expenditure for the next financial year is being planned.
HOW?	<ul><li>Separate research and education costs.</li><li>Use a simple system of classification such as the International Classification of Diseases (ICD).</li><li>Allocate all other costs to the programme budgets proportionally, including primary care, laboratory and imaging.</li><li>Distribute the budget analysis.</li><li>Respond to criticisms by asking for suggestions about how allocation can be improved, but also by reminding people that it is their data and any quality problems start with them!</li><li>For each budget, payers and managers should ask what would be the effect on the value derived from resources if we:<ul><li>increased the allocation to this programme by 5%?</li><li>decreased the allocation to this budget by 5%?</li></ul></li><li>Produce a report of these discussions and a proposal for reallocation of resources for the next financial year.</li></ul>

WHAT?	*How to conduct a review of expenditure on a disease*
WHY?	Because the main focus of healthcare management, competition, and value improvement, should be on diseases, such as breast cancer, not on hospitals or insurance schemes.
WHO?	All those involved in managing resources for a particular condition – patients' representatives, and payers.
WHEN?	Because this activity requires energy and focus, and, since there are about fifty 'big' problems such as epilepsy or diabetes, plan one a week throughout the year.
HOW?	<ul><li>Produce a value review pack containing data on:<ul><li>○ hospital admissions compared with other services;</li><li>○ prescribing rates compared with other services;</li><li>○ outcome data, if available;</li><li>○ any other data on variations in the care provided, from audit studies, for example;</li><li>○ financial data, if available;</li><li>○ new high quality evidence produced in the preceding year.</li></ul></li><li>Present the pack to a workshop.</li><li>Accept criticisms of the data, reminding participants that 'These are the data you submitted.'</li><li>Ask the workshop to focus on their existing resources and ask:<ul><li>○ what should we do more of, or better?</li><li>○ what should we do less?</li></ul></li><li>Ask the workshop to advise:<ul><li>○ what would be their top priority if new money became available;</li><li>○ what would be their lowest priority if cuts had to be made.</li></ul></li></ul>

WHAT?	*How to manage knowledge*
WHY?	Because the implementation of what we know from research, from data, and from experience will have a bigger impact on health and healthcare than any other drug or technology likely to be developed in the next decade.
WHO?	The Chief Executive, Boards and Management Teams.
WHEN?	The management of knowledge needs to be reported to Executive Boards and Management Teams as frequently as financial reports.
HOW?	<ul><li>The Chief Executive should identify one Board Member as responsible for knowledge and give that person the responsibility of being the Chief Knowledge Officer (CKO).</li><li>Each significant management team in the organisation should also have one person on that team responsible for getting knowledge into practice.</li><li>A librarian should be free from library management duties to support the CKO.</li><li>Require the CKO to prepare a plan, describing how:<ul><li>the knowledge coming into the organisation can be improved;</li><li>more knowledge from experience can be created within the organisation;</li><li>important new knowledge can be more effectively implemented;</li><li>the knowledge produced by the organisation, e.g. patient leaflets, can be improved.</li></ul></li><li>Implement the plan.</li></ul>

WHAT?	*How to manage innovation*
WHY?	Because organisations and individuals often adopt low value interventions while failing to develop or introduce high value interventions, unless innovation is managed.
WHO?	Every healthcare organisation that has a budget should have an Innovation Group, supported by the Chief Knowledge Officer and a librarian.
WHEN?	The group should meet regularly and produce an Annual Report.
HOW?	<ul><li>Write a remit for the Innovation Group emphasising that:<ul><li>its primary remit is to promote the development of new ways of working and to introduce new high value ideas from elsewhere;</li><li>its second priority is to promote research and evaluation and ensure that new services or interventions of uncertain value are introduced only in the context of research;</li><li>its third priority is to ensure that interventions of low value, new tests, new treatments, or new services are not introduced.</li></ul></li><li>Appoint an influential clinician as the Chair.</li><li>Provide some resources to fund evaluations and encourage evaluators to publish their results.</li><li>Ask the Chief Knowledge Officer and librarian to provide support to the group.</li><li>Give the group one or two innovations that will be introduced on their recommendation in the first year.</li><li>Support innovation schemes with rewards for teams who innovate to produce better value.</li><li>Present an Annual Innovation Report to the Board.</li></ul>

WHAT?	*How to reduce the number of errors*
WHY?	Because errors cause harm to patients, and costs to healthcare.
WHEN?	This needs to be a continuous process, but should have both an annual cycle, and specific actions as serious errors are identified.
WHO?	This needs to be a responsibility of every person who manages resources.
HOW?	<ul><li>Promote continuous quality improvement, because improvement in quality will reduce the incidence of errors.</li><li>Ask the Chief Knowledge Officer to review the knowledge about the types of errors likely to occur, and the evidence about the interventions which reduce risk.</li><li>Set up a Risk Reduction Group, with a clearly accountable leader.</li><li>Ask the group to develop and implement a risk reduction plan.</li><li>Ensure there is a clear protocol for the investigation of errors, and the method by which patients can be involved in resolving problems caused by errors.</li></ul>

WHAT?	*How to engage patients and improve their experience*
WHY?	Because the engagement of patients will improve the value of healthcare.
WHEN?	This is a continuous process, part of general management, but an annual patient engagement conference can highlight and focus this process.
WHO?	Every person who manages resources needs to be given this as a clear responsibility.
HOW?	<ul><li>A person who can speak as a patient should be enrolled on the Board or management team.</li><li>Review and improve complaint management.</li><li>Use the immediate feedback offered by www.iwantgreatcare.org.</li><li>Reduce resources used in measuring patient satisfaction, and increase resources used to measure patient experience.</li><li>Either develop your own patient experience questionnaire or commission an agency to conduct the surveys.</li><li>Review the written information given to patients, and assure and improve the quality by adopting the Information Standard – www.informationstandard.org.</li><li>Ensure managers conduct experience surveys at least once a year and act on results; high quality surveys done for a short period are better value than continuous poor quality surveys.</li></ul>

WHAT?	*How to improve productivity*
WHY?	Because increased productivity frees resources for high value healthcare without adverse effects.
WHEN?	Continuously, obsessionally, but highlighted by an Annual Productivity Workshop and celebrations.
WHO?	Every person who manages resources. A Productivity Interest Group (PIG) to generate and support ideas can pull together leads from all the divisions (PIGs are very productive creatures!).

HOW?	• Ensure that everyone is clear about the distinction between efficiency and productivity, and that productivity does not mean a reduction in quality but an improvement in value.
	
	• Develop and implement a communication plan.
	
	• Set up projects to:
	   ○ make more use of buildings and equipment;
	   ○ improve procurement;
	   ○ reduce stock;
	   ○ launch a hospital-at-home project;
	   ○ reduce the use of paper;
	   ○ prevent the waste of resources on poor value research;
	   ○ make better use of the time of the most experienced staff.
	
	• Require an Annual Productivity Report.

WHAT?	*How to increase effectiveness*
WHY?	Because increased effectiveness increases value.
WHO?	Clinical leaders, including those in imaging, pharmacy and laboratory services, and all people who manage resources.
WHEN?	Continuous process, built into annual planning and reporting of the same status as finance.
HOW?	• Set up an Innovation Group to ensure that no ineffective technology slips into use. • Require the Chief Knowledge Officer to produce monthly knowledge briefings about new evidence that should be put into practice. • Develop systems of care, with care pathways for all common procedures and conditions, using software such as the Map of Medicine (www.mapofmedicine.com). • For each condition, ask the relevant clinical lead to identify evidence-based measures of process and outcome measures of relevance to patients. • Require each service to produce an Annual Effectiveness Plan, based on the annual review of their service and care. • Require all Annual Reports to describe effectiveness compared with performance of other services and explicit national standards. • Introduce the methods of continuous quality improvement.

WHAT?	*How to get to the root of problems*
WHY?	Because short-term solutions to immediate causes are of lower value than solutions which tackle root causes.
WHO?	Whoever has a problem.
WHEN?	Whenever there is a problem or an opportunity for value improvement that 'can't be done'.
HOW?	Use the Five Whys method of Taiichi Ohno, who always asked 'Why?' five times, for example:

• Why is this patient at the clinic?	Because we have the reports of his investigations.
• Why could the results not be sent to him?	Because a clinical decision needs to be made.
• Why could he not make that decision with his primary care physician?	Because the physician does not know how we manage this problem.
• Why does she not know how this problem is managed? Is it too difficult?	No it is not too difficult, but she is new to the area and not familiar with how we do things.
• Why do we not identify and brief new GPs about our procedures?	'Good question.'

WHAT?	*How to carry out a systematic review*
WHY?	A systematic review of all the evidence is necessary to minimise bias and errors in reports of research.
WHO?	The scale of a systematic review, and the skills required, should not be underestimated. Those who pay for or manage healthcare should commission someone who has experience to do the review.
WHEN?	Before significant resources are invested.
HOW?	<ul><li>Make the question as precise as possible – e.g. instead of asking for a systematic review of PET scanners, ask 'What is the added value of PET scanning for patients with advanced cancer?'</li><li>Search the scientific literature with the assistance of a librarian and keep a copy of the search strategy.</li><li>Use explicit quality criteria to decide which research reports should be included in the review and which should be excluded.</li><li>Ask a statistician how the data in the individual high quality research reports should be combined.</li><li>Publish the results of the review, including the references to the reports that were excluded for reasons of quality as well as the references of reports included in the review.</li></ul>

WHAT?	*How to transform healthcare using information technology*
WHY?	There are two reasons. Firstly, because the technology creates tools that by themselves change culture and practice – reflect on the lessons of history as described by Lynn White Jnr. in *Medieval Technology and Social Change.* Secondly, because investing in information technology simply to do the same things digitally is of very low value – reflect on the lessons of 'How New Technologies Cause Great Companies To Fail' in *The Innovator's Dilemma* by Clayton Christensen.
WHO?	Everyone must be involved, but someone needs to take the lead in 'The Transformation of Care', not a project called 'The Introduction of IT'.
WHEN?	Before every investment in IT.
HOW?	<ul><li>Send the patient information digitally, linked to email if they have it, on a DVD if they do not, before and after every consultation.</li><li>Encourage patients to record the consultation on their mobile phones.</li><li>Offer email consultations.</li><li>Train clinicians how to consult well with a computer in the consulting room.</li><li>Describe all care pathways and standard operating procedures digitally, using the Map of Medicine software.</li><li>Use IT to help multidisciplinary teams work smarter.</li><li>Make all knowledge available online.</li><li>Create clinical networks which are sustained on the web, not by a bureaucracy.</li><li>Put laboratory IT in charge of chronic disease monitoring.</li><li>Get the Chief Executive to create a blog.</li></ul>

Questions for reflection when teaching or developing networks

If using these in network building or teaching, give one of the questions to the group and ask them to work in pairs to reflect on the question for three minutes; try to get people who do not know one another to work together.

When taking feedback, let each pair make only one point. In the interests of equity, if you start with the pair on the left-hand side of the room for the first question, start with the pair on the right-hand side of the room for the second question.

- How could the Why? Who? When? How? structure be made more useful?
- Which challenges do we face that we could deconstruct using this approach?
- Which of the challenges listed above should we tackle using this method?

6

LEADING THE CHANGE TO BETTER VALUE

This chapter will:

- define the contribution of leadership to increasing value;
- emphasise the need for transformation, not reorganisation;
- describe how change is tackled in industry.

By the end of the chapter you will understand:

- how a sense of urgency needs to be created if not present;
- the benefits of disruption as opposed to gradual change;
- the need to think of the frontline clinician at least as much as high strategy.

The book so far has described a method that will derive more value from the resources invested in health services, a method that will be essential for the 21st century when the rate of growth of investment in health services will slow, or stop, or perhaps even reverse. But how will the change be brought about? Not just by an intellectual exercise, that's for sure; what is required is leadership of the highest order.

It is, however, difficult to say what the leader will do. Firstly, we need to identify the focus of the leader's efforts and a simple model of the aspects of a health service is shown below (Figure 6.1).

Figure 6.1 Model of a health service

One reason why it is difficult to define what the leader should do is because there is no agreed definition of the job of the leader, but there are two aspects of leadership that are commonly agreed.

The first thing is to change the culture of the organisation, and the 2010 White Paper, *Equity and Excellence: Liberating the NHS,* was a document which aimed to change culture at least as much as it aimed to describe the proposed managerial changes. For example, by emph- asising that the NHS would be led by frontline staff, and by including in the section on 'The Information Revolution' patient feedback as a type of information that would change the service, it also recognised that behaviour change by itself can stimulate cultural change. The commitment to 'reduce management costs by 45% over the next four years' will change the culture and encourage innovation because there will be fewer people asking frontline staff to fill in forms.

The second job of the leader is to help people come to terms with bad news, and both of these tasks merge in the one task of transformation. The leader has to help their organisation change from one that is based on the assumption that there will always be more money to one that assumes that there will be no more money. The fact of the matter is that many people who should be leaders change the structure instead of building systems and changing the culture, but the job of the leader is clear.

The news is in fact not as bad as it seems at first glance. By creating more value from the resources available, the leader will help their organisation become sustainable, a key 21st century objective and one that is morally important as well as economically sensible.

But how is the leader to do this? There are as many books on this subject as there are on the nature of leadership. John P. Kotter, one of the most highly respected authors on the subject, lists eight key steps for the leader.

1. Establishing a sense of urgency
2. Creating a guiding coalition
3. Developing a vision and strategy
4. Communicating the change vision

5. Empowering employees for broad based action
6. Generating short-term wins
7. Consolidating gains and producing more change
8. Anchoring new approaches in the culture (1)

His most recent book's title, *The Sense of Urgency* (2), indicates that he has found the first step the most difficult. The economic crunch has helped, but in healthcare there is still the assumption that the old ways will continue somehow. The leader has to change that and they do this by using a number of interventions, simultaneously and in sequence, so that they can benefit from the Hawthorne Effect, namely the effect that almost every innovation has on quality because of the effect it has on the psyche of the workforce. These include the development of clinical systems and networks, the introduction of appropriate technology, patient engagement, and a variety of industrial methods such as Lean or Six Sigma. They have to be prepared for a long haul and the final words to would-be leaders by John Black, who has applied *The Toyota Way* to healthcare with success, are:

1. You have to continue to personally lead the charge
2. A master sensei is almost essential
3. You must be willing to commit to a long term 'slog' through the swamp of waste and defects that lie beneath the surface of your daily operations.(3)

The most radical call to arms comes from Clayton Christensen, whose work examines and supports the iconoclastic impact of new technology. His most famous work is *The Innovator's Dilemma* subtitled *When New Technologies Cause Great Companies to Fail.* (4) In this he emphasised the need to recognise the disruptive effects of new technology, the way in which it could transform an industry, reducing cost, improving quality and increasing access. In his latest book *The Innovator's Prescription* he and two medical co-authors describe *A Disruptive Solution for Health Care.* (5) They propose 'Disruptive Value Networks', focused on single conditions and delivering end to end care for people with chronic disease. Programme budgeting would enable this to happen but it could act against the short term interests of hospitals. Hospitals have a crucial role to play as 'Solution Shops' sorting out complicated problems and reaching a diagnosis, but they are only a node in a network. New technology, genetic profiling to personalise care, and the Internet to manage it, can, with the power of patients, drive this transformation.

The White Paper *Equity and Excellence: Liberating the NHS,* is also an example of a disruptive innovation. It states that general practitioners will be given lead responsibility in commissioning health service but does not specify exactly how this will happen; nor does it state that many general practitioners oppose this proposal; but the importance of the proposal is its disruptive effect, not only on existing structures but, even more important, on the existing culture.

Finally, it is essential to remember that no matter how elegant the systems and how robust the culture, success depends on, in the words of William Slim, *'the high quality of the individual soldier, his morale, toughness and discipline, his acceptance of hardship and his ability to move on his own feet and to look after himself'* (6). It is the frontline healthcare professionals and patients who deliver better value healthcare. 40,000 consultations and 200,000 clinical decisions are made each day for every million population, and that is where resources are used and value produced.

The 21st century needs both good judgement and good leaders; it needs healthcare based on systems, not institutions, and it needs a new culture.

> ## Questions for reflection when teaching or developing networks
>
> If using these in network building or teaching, give one of the questions to the group and ask them to work in pairs to reflect on the question for three minutes; try to get people who do not know one another to work together.
>
> When taking feedback, let each pair make only one point. In the interests of equity, if you start with the pair on the left-hand side of the room for the first question, start with the pair on the right-hand side of the room for the second question.
>
> - What disruptive technologies could accelerate change? Discuss the universal availability of smart phones.
> - Reflect on one successful and one unsuccessful change programme.
> - How could you contribute to change for better value more effectively?

References

(1)   Kotter, J.P. (1996) *Leading Change*. Harvard University Press.

(2)   Kotter, J.P. (2008) *Sense of Urgency*. Harvard University Press.

(3)   Black, J. and Miller, D. (2006) *The Toyota Way to Healthcare Excellence*. Health Administration Press.

(4)   Christensen, C.M. (1997) *The Innovator's Dilemma; When New Technologies Cause Great Companies To Fail*. HBS Press.

(5)   Christensen, C.M, Grossman, J.H. and Hwang, J. (2008) *The Innovator's Prescription; A Disruptive Solution for Health Care*. McGraw-Hill.

(6)   Slim, W. (1956) *Defeat Into Victory*. Cooper Square Press.

Index

AIDS, 3
allocation of resources, 61, 62, 68, 78, 120
annual population value review, 120
annual productivity report, 126
Archie Cochrane, v, 28
Avedis Donabedian, 95
benefits, 6, 20, 28, 29, 31, 33, 41, 46, 50, 51, 63, 74, 94, 99, 119
bounded rationality, 69
carbon reduction, 9
Centre for Sustainable Healthcare, 110
Chief Knowledge Officer, 122, 123, 124, 127
Chief Medical Officer, 99
children
    allocation of resources, 68
    equitable allocation to, 67
communication plan, 126
cost inflation, 8
cost-effectiveness, 26, 28, 29, 61, 69, 74, 76
costs, 7, 8, 17, 33, 44, 91, 102, 108, 110
DALY, 21, 61
decision making, 69, 81, 82, 85, 87, 88
demand, 1, 4, 32, 85
Disease Impact Number, 61
disinvestment, 65
distributive justice, 69, 78
drift, 82
    industry driven, 85
    technology driven, 83

drugs, 7, 29, 47, 74, 85, 102
education, 43
    value of, 45
effectiveness, 1, 25, 26, 28, 74, 91
    how to increase, 127
efficiency, 26, 104
    allocative, 60, 63
    technical, 61
Equity and Excellence, 2, 40, 44, 45, 50, 60, 69, 93, 101, 102, 106, 109, 115, 133, 135
errors, 74, 98, 99
    reduction, 124
ethnicity, 67
Evidence-Based Medicine, 6, 26, 47
framing, 6, 76
GNP, 38
harm, 6, 26, 27, 30, 51, 72, 75, 81, 98, 99, 102
ICER, 77
industry, 9, 18, 134
information, 6, 52, 59, 63, 125, 133
Information Revolution, 52, 115, 133
information technology, 10
innovation, 7, 8, 52, 76, 119, 123, 133, 134
Innovator's Prescription, 11, 52, 54, 134, 136
insurance, 38, 39
Internet, 4, 10, 52, 53, 134
Jack Wennberg, 87, 88
judgement, 38, 69, 76, 78, 86, 87, 135